Additional Praise for *Paper* W9-DFQ-218

"The technologies described in this book can turn bits of data into actionable information that will lead to medical knowledge and wisdom. This is the pathway to 21st-century personalized medicine and the process of continuous learning that is essential to improve healthcare and save lives."

—**Andrew C. von Eschenbach, M.D.,** Former Commissioner, Food and Drug Administration; Former Director, National Cancer Institute

"Doctors and nurses cannot make sound decisions with their patients without information, from the latest breakthroughs in treatments to recent lab tests, prescription histories, and other vital information. Community-wide, interconnected IT is the only tool that can deliver the right information at the right place at the right time."

—**Pat Fry,** President and CEO, Sutter Health

"Electronic health records are ultimately about improved quality and better, more consistent outcomes. This includes expediting research to bring new therapies to patients. I truly believe that this untapped potential will change how we develop and deliver better medicine. This timely and thorough book provides a powerful exploration of the technologies that can and will transform healthcare."

—**Justin T. Barnes,** Chairman, Electronic Health Record Association; Vice President, Greenway Medical Technologies

"It is long past time to modernize healthcare. Health plans, consumers, and providers must embrace health IT to save lives and save money."

—**Malik Hasan, M.D.,** President and CEO, HealthTrio

"Information management will be the common ground in healthcare transformation in both the clinical and policy arenas. Once again David Merritt addresses the subject with clarity and acumen. Physicians at all stages of their careers, from residents to mature clinicians, will benefit from David's insight and clear presentation."

—**Michael C. Burgess, M.D.,** Member of the United States House of Representatives (R-TX); Chair, Congressional Health Care Caucus

"Health information technology is vital to helping doctors and patients live healthy and fight chronic disease. It is also vital to finding ways to prevent disease in the first place. I applaud the expertise and experiences highlighted in this important book to help make this happen."

—**Julie Louise Gerberding, M.D., M.P.H.,** Former Director,
Centers for Disease Control and Prevention

"Gundersen's success is due to great people, sound processes, and smart technology. From regional clinics to specialty care such as the breast or cardiac center, health IT has been essential in delivering high-quality care and lowering costs. If we would more rapidly embrace the lessons included in this book, our country's future would be much brighter."

—**Jeff Thompson, M.D.,** Chief Executive Officer,
Gundersen Lutheran Health System

"Transforming healthcare is about making positive, informed decisions. Today's system is a barrier to good choices, for employers, doctors, payers, and patients alike. Health IT can fix that. By exchanging data and gaining actionable knowledge, we can improve quality and lower costs. This book makes a valuable contribution by showing us how to do it."

—**Sreedhar Potaratzu, M.D., M.B.A.,** President and CEO,
VitalSpring Technologies; Author of *Get Off the Dime:
The Secret of Changing Who Pays for Your Healthcare*

"This impressive collection of materials from healthcare leaders from every industry sector will help us tackle the complex and critical issues we must resolve to ensure an efficient, high quality, modern health system. In particular, the pieces on improving health information infrastructure point the way toward common sense, bipartisan reforms that can make healthcare better and more accessible."

—**Sheldon Whitehouse,** Member of the United States Senate (D-RI)

"The technologies addressed in *Paper Kills 2.0* have the potential to help to truly transform our public health system. From treating and preventing disease to eliminating disparities in care, an interconnected, coordinated system is essential."

—**David Satcher, M.D., Ph.D.,** Director,
The Satcher Health Leadership Institute and Center of Excellence on
Health Disparities, Morehouse School of Medicine;
16th Surgeon General of the United States

Other Center for Health Transformation Books

The Art of Transformation by Newt Gingrich and Nancy Desmond

Making Medicaid Work by CHT and SHPS

Saving Lives & Saving Money by Newt Gingrich, with Dana Pavey and Anne Woodbury

Paper Kills Edited by David Merritt

Stop Paying the Crooks: Solutions to End the Fraud That Threatens Your Healthcare Edited by James Frogue

Available at www.healthtransformation.net

CHT Press
1425 K Street, NW
Suite 450
Washington, D.C. 20005

President and CEO: Nancy Desmond
Communications Coordinator: Alissa Momberg

© 2010 by the Center for Health Transformation

Printed in the United States of America.

All rights reserved.

Internet address: www.healthtransformation.net

No part of this publication may be reproduced, stored in retrieval system, or transmitted in any form or by any means electronic, mechanical, photocopying, recording or otherwise, without the prior written permission of the publisher.

Additional copies of this book may be ordered by calling 202-375-2001 or visiting the CHT website at www.healthtransformation.net.

ISBN 978-1-933966-08-3

The authors, editors, and publisher of this work have checked with sources believed to be reliable in their efforts to confirm the accuracy and completeness of the information presented. However, neither the authors nor the publisher nor any party involved in the creation and publication of this work warrant that the information is in every respect accurate and complete, and they are not responsible for any errors or omissions or for any consequences from application of the information in this book.

Information provided in this book is for educational and demonstration purposes and is not intended to constitute legal advice. If legal advice is required, the services of a competent professional should be sought. All comments, opinions, and observations are those of the authors, and do not represent official positions or opinions unless specifically noted.

Paper Kills 2.0

How Health IT Can Help Save Your Life and Your Money

Edited by David Merritt

Peter Neupert · Brent James, M.D. · Marc Probst
Brandon Savage, M.D. · Sarah T. Corley, M.D., F.A.C.P
Charles W. Jarvis, F.A.C.H.E. · Thomas J. Miller · Ben Sawyer
Jim Rosenblum · Chad A. Eckes · Julie D. Klapstein
Wyche "Tee" Green III · Jason Colquitt · Robert M. Barthelmes
Timothy M. Elwell · Kate Berry · Jac J. Davies
Nancy L. Vorhees · Harris A. Frankel, M.D. · Deborah Bass

Published by CHT Press

Acknowledgements

Thank you to Newt Gingrich for his tireless leadership, vision, and dedication to transforming health and healthcare.

Special thanks and appreciation go to members of the Center for Health Transformation, who show us every day that transformation is possible.

Special thanks go to Alissa Momberg and Vincent Frakes for their tremendous work on this book and to Nancy Desmond for her continued leadership of CHT.

Paper Kills 2.0

How Health IT Can Help Save Your Life and Your Money

Edited by David Merritt

Foreword

by Newt Gingrich and Tom Daschle

—⁓—

Think of the first time you saw an iPhone in action. Or the first time you browsed the Internet or the first PC you bought. What did you think? Most of us were probably blown away. We intuitively knew that we held something transformational.

What do you think when you see a paper medical record? Rather than the excitement of innovation and progress, it's typically something like, "Do I really have to fill this form out again?" And that's just the convenience factor. Most of us are unaware of the price we pay for both lower-quality care and higher costs.

Just think of it: we administer the largest, most complex, and arguably the most important sector of our economy with manila envelopes—even though our lives and well-being are at stake. According to a national survey in the *New England Journal of Medicine*, a scant 4 percent of physicians use advanced electronic medical records.[1] Not only is it virtually impossible to fix our system's current problems with paper records, but they are a main cause of and contributor to alarming rates of medical errors, breathtaking levels of waste, and perpetually rising costs.

These problems and more are why moving healthcare into the 21st century through health information technology (HIT) is so essential. And the benefits are clear. Updated, accurate, and comprehensive patient information at the point of care will prevent medical errors and will allow physicians, nurses, and providers to make better, more informed decisions. Electronic access to information will reduce duplicative and unnecessary tests and treatments. Automating cumbersome, manual processes will streamline workflow, eliminate inefficiencies, and lower costs. These are facts.

Thankfully, the argument over whether such a transformation is necessary is largely over. Yes, there are those who will try to cling to the past, holding on to what is familiar, but they too will ultimately be convinced. Just as the automobile replaced the horse and buggy, just as personal computers overtook mainframes, and just as cell phones have made pay phones virtually obsolete, so too will health IT transform the way we deliver and administer healthcare. It is not only the right thing to do to improve care and lower costs—it is the inevitable march of progress.

President Barack Obama and his administration deserve tremendous credit for advancing this vital issue. Moving health information technology forward was the very first healthcare reform of his presidency. While some questioned whether the investment should have been included in the stimulus legislation, billions of dollars were included in the *American Recovery and Reinvestment Act of 2009* as a down payment to move physicians and providers into the 21st century.

The Eisenhower Model

It often takes decisive presidential leadership to tackle a challenge on this scale. As a student of history, President Obama has spoken often about looking to his predecessors for guidance. When it comes to health IT, he has taken a page from our 34th president, Dwight D. Eisenhower.

Eisenhower faced many of the same problems in the mid-20th century when he envisioned a nationwide interstate highway system. That creation, which now bears his name, remains one of the most significant accomplishments in American history. While such a system had long been a dream, it was Eisenhower who made it a reality when he proposed and then signed the *Federal Aid Highway Act of 1956*, beginning the construction of more than 41,000 miles of interstate highways.

Eisenhower described the nation's roads prior to the highway system as "an appalling problem of waste, danger, and death." This is an apt description of our healthcare system today. Presidential leadership can change this, and President Obama is applying the same lessons that Eisenhower did more than a half-century ago to achieve success.

First, President Eisenhower made a significant financial commitment. In 1956, Congress appropriated $25 billion for highway construction, which was a vast sum of money considering that total federal spending in 1956 was $70 billion. Hundreds of billions of dollars were eventually spent, making it one of the nation's highest priorities.

President Obama will invest more than $20 billion to place information technology in the hands of doctors and providers. The primary vehicle for this investment is through incentive payments from Medicare or Medicaid—up to $64,000 per physician—for the "meaningful use" of certified technology. Health and Human Services (HHS) Secretary Kathleen Sebelius and the National Coordinator for Health Information Technology, David Blumenthal, were right to make the meaningful use criteria quality- or outcomes-based. Simply automating manual processes is not transformational, but tying meaningful use incentives to clinical performance measures can be.

This should be a model moving forward. We need to fundamentally change the way we pay for healthcare services. Incentivizing the use of technology should ultimately give way to paying for better quality care, not just for the quantity of services.

Second, President Eisenhower created an interconnected system. One of the most important components of the interstate highway system was its adherence to uniform standards of construction. According to the Federal Highway Administration, common standards included 12-foot lane widths, standard shoulder widths, a minimum of two travel lanes in each direction, and speed limits. They built a true system that avoided each state building its own highways with its own unique specifications.

We run a similar risk in healthcare. If billions are spent to equip doctors and hospitals with technologies that cannot communicate with each other, we will have laid a lot of track that does not connect. In addition to the "meaningful use" criteria, HHS is also narrowing the technology standards or specifications of how to exchange electronic information, as well as finalizing the process of private-sector product certification. While the progress on standards and certification could have been bolder, clearer, and faster, it is still progress nonetheless.

Third, President Eisenhower created a true collaboration among the private sector, states, and the federal government through highway construction. Even though the federal government paid 90 percent of the costs of building the highway system, the states were responsible for managing the construction, and the private sector did the actual work.

Building upon the leadership, progress, and foundation laid by former HHS secretaries Mike Leavitt and Tommy Thompson, as well as former National Coordinator David Brailer, President Obama has made public-private collaboration a cornerstone of his efforts. From the Beacon Community Program, which will accelerate and advance the connectivity efforts already under way in many communities across the country, to working with state governments, the federal government can and should support new and existing efforts of state and local leaders working with the private sector.

Eisenhower's leadership created a wave of productivity and prosperity that we continue to ride today. It opened new markets through interstate commerce, created a national sense of community, brought the modern world to rural America, enabled families to move and travel over long distances, and drove innovation from coast to coast. We can experience that same level of transformation in healthcare through information technology.

This book captures the progress that has already been made and the future within our grasp. From innovation, personalized medicine, and medical homes to open source, telemedicine, and cancer care, we can transform our system to one that saves lives and saves money for all Americans.

That is everyone's goal, regardless of political party. Despite agreement on the broad goals of improving care and lowering costs, the past year has shown that finding common ground can be very challenging. While it is important for policymakers to stand their ground when they must, it is equally as important to have the courage to collaborate when they should. Health information technology is one of those issues.

With even more difficult challenges upon us, from Medicare solvency to workforce shortages, this must be the first of many priorities where Republicans, Democrats, and Independents can join together to solve the problems we face. It has happened before, and it must happen again. Our country and our future depend on it.

Newt Gingrich and Tom Daschle
January 2010

—⁂—

[1] Catherine M. DesRoches, Eric G. Campbell, et al., "Electronic Health Records in Ambulatory Care: A National Survey of Physicians," *New England Journal of Medicine*, Vol. 359:50-60, July 3, 2008, No. 1., http://content.nejm.org/content/vol359/issue1/index.dtl.

CHAPTER 1

Recharting Healthcare: Innovations to Drive a New Delivery Model for Tomorrow's Health System

Peter Neupert

—w—

Editor's Introduction

"We see a future in which consumers are in control of their own healthcare, providers have exactly the information they need and can focus on prevention and personalized care, and healthcare becomes a learning system of constant improvement."[1] This is the vision at Microsoft's Health Solutions Group, and one that should be embraced by everyone. It is not about tweaking a broken system. It is about transforming it into a system that delivers better quality care at lower cost for every American. Innovation is the heart of this transformation, which today is often suffocated by the burdensome regulations, atrophied precedents, and sheer complexity of today's system. However, health information technology is not only an innovation; it is also a liberator. It can free consumers from confusion and the unknown and empower them to make informed decisions. It allows providers to deliver the best possible care to their patients, with less paperwork and more efficiency. Through the combination of innovation, technology, and profound structural changes, such as payment reform, we can turn this vision of transformation into reality.

—w—

It is ironic that while there have been so many advances in medicine—robotic-assisted surgery, the cloning of embryos, the mapping of genomes—our health delivery model has remained essentially the same.[2] We call the doctor, make an appointment, go to the office, fill out the paper forms (in rare cases, they are electronic), wait, answer a nurse's questions, answer the same questions for the doctor, go to the pharmacy to fill a prescription, go home, and likely do not see the doctor again until we are sick once more—at which point we repeat the process all over again. In no other industry do we basically "do it" the same way we "did it" years ago.

Unfortunately, the consequence of our inability to change is reflected in the high price we pay for healthcare. Today, Americans spend $7,290 per person on health expenditures—more than double what any other developed nation spends. Instead of finding and furthering efficiency gains, American healthcare seems to have foregone them.[3]

Our health delivery model has simply not evolved to keep up with today's and tomorrow's reality. Our nation's health has changed, but our current delivery model has remained what is essentially an acute, episodic care business model from the 19th century, a traditional fee-for-service model based on patients visiting hospitals and physicians' offices only when they are sick.[4] Further, health is fundamentally a data problem and will become increasingly so with advances in personalized medicine, but our delivery system has not progressed to use data in an effective way to drive better decision-making and improved methods. Face it: Expedia, an organization that has to connect to thousands of different organizations and data sources, likely knows more about its travel sales nationally *in real time* than a hospital does about common procedures like hip replacements in its own facility.

We have been locked into the past primarily because the regulations and mindsets governing healthcare have carved this fee-for-service model into stone. This has inhibited the kind of broad-scale innovation that has transformed nearly every other industry that touches our lives—complex, expensive products and services once available to few have become accessible and affordable for the masses.[5] We need this same kind of paradigm shift in health to keep up with the changes in disease and advances in medicine and to stop skyrocketing costs.

What is needed is a new framework that enables innovation, rewards experimentation, and ultimately drives value. This is what will allow us to realize the policy goals of providing increased access, maintaining fiscal responsibility, and delivering on the promise of personalized medicine.

The Current Pulse of Healthcare

In the early 20th century, infection was the leading cause of death in the United States.[6] Acute in nature, infections were treated as they emerged. Over time, as we learned more about these diseases and their causes, we were able to precisely treat them. The result was a dramatic reduction in overall healthcare costs. Diseases like tuberculosis, cholera, and malaria, which once accounted for the bulk of overall costs, are now but a tiny portion.[7] As the century progressed, however, infection gave way to chronic disease as the leading cause of death and the primary driver of health costs in the United States.[8]

The shift has significantly impacted healthcare today because most chronic diseases require a lifetime of ongoing care, in contrast to acute care upon which the current system is based. The U.S. Centers for Disease Control and Prevention now estimate that more than 75 percent of America's healthcare costs stems from six chronic disease states.[9] And the number of people with chronic diseases continues to rise. Today, about 133 million Americans (nearly half of all adults) live with at least one chronic illness.[10]

If we are to reverse these trends, we need to focus on wellness and health "management" to ensure that patients follow a treatment over the course of their lives and do not end up in the most expensive care setting—the emergency room—on a regular basis. Managing these diseases requires monitoring and interacting with patients daily or weekly to check drug and test regimens to help patients make better choices and to change behaviors over the long term.

And as a part of this, we have to encourage individuals to be more accountable for and sensitive to the care they are receiving. An individual's many behavioral choices can dramatically alter the cost of healthcare over the course of his or her life. Obesity alone, for example, costs the health system $147 billion a year and obesity-related conditions now account for nearly 10 percent of all medical spending.[11] Obesity is also one of the biggest risk factors for developing the chronic diseases that drive the majority of direct and indirect costs to our system, including diabetes cardiovascular disease, and stroke. Obesity is within our control to manage, but there is not any incentive to do so. It is critical to align incentives, economic or otherwise, to drive change. The status quo will only doom us to continue the cycle of out-of-control healthcare spending.

Regrettably, the health delivery system is not designed for this type of health management and real-time consumer engagement. Vital to this is the movement of data across the continuum of care, from the physician's office to the patient's home and anywhere in between. But today, data is almost exclusively collected at the point of care (the physician's office or hospital), locked away in various paper or (maybe) electronic files, and simply does not play a role in a consumer's decision-making process. Further, today's payment system does not compensate physicians for health outcomes or innovation.[12]

A good example is a diabetic. Diabetics must monitor blood sugar levels regularly and see multiple physicians as well as other healthcare professionals such as nutritionists or therapists.[13] To maximize a diabetic's care, each person on the care team should have access to all the data available about the patient: blood sugar levels, lab work, dietary or fitness information, and so on. They should also be compensated to drive better health outcomes and be able to innovate with new services to keep that individual on track with his or her treatment.

Other sectors have changed with the times. If you think about how you manage your finances, you can do it anywhere you can access the Internet—your cell phone, PC, office, and bank. Now, more than 53 million Americans use online banking to pay bills, transfer funds, and check their balances.[14] Even sports have changed to allow people to have access to information in real time—from fantasy football statistics to tracking marathon race progress.[15] Imagine how transformative it could be for people to have their own health data and use it in real time to help set fitness goals, manage their blood sugar levels or blood pressure, and take control of their health.

Resuscitating Healthcare

We need to transition healthcare from unmanaged care (show up when you are sick, "fee-for-service") to informed, coordinated care (population focus and pay for outcome), and from unman-aged processes (treat in office/hospital, based on physician) to managed processes (assuring that patients follow a care pathway; drug and test regimen across time and location). In order to drive this change and reform healthcare, we need to focus on a few key areas to create a foundation for the future.

Take the Variation Out of Care by Creating Feedback Loops
Toyota has shown us that if we do a task differently every time, we will not be able to improve the result.[16] In health, this is about using data to see what works, and then educating medical professionals and consumers to put the best methods into practice. With chronic diseases, we have some well-understood approaches to care, and as we learn more, we need feedback loops that can help improve treat-ments and drive behavioral change in a reasonable time frame. An example of an organization starting to develop feedback loops is the Cleveland Clinic. The organization has focused on remote patient monitoring utilizing home healthcare devices with nearly 400 patients. The clinic is disrupting the current care model by bringing near-real time remote monitoring to patients and their providers. The result? Reporting health status no longer means waiting for the next appointment with a physician. While the final results of the study are not yet known, the hope that is tighter feedback loops between physicians and patients will improve outcomes.

Today's system, however, does not broadly support this kind of knowledge transfer. It takes months to collect data about proce-dures, let alone analyze the information and turn it into consistent practice. Further, the opinion of one physician, whose treatment may call for multiple tests, procedures, and the like, is what dictates a course of action. A more effective approach would be to lever-age data to determine effective treatments, called "evidence-based" medicine. We cannot control or manage costs effectively until we know what works.

Encourage and Stimulate Supply-Side Innovation
Our current fee-for-service payment model does not reinforce and reward provider innovation, nor does it facilitate new industry entrants to drive better, more efficient, convenient, and cost-effective delivery methods.[17] Most innovation today is happening at integrated

systems like Geisinger Health System or Kaiser Permanente.[18] They represent both payer and provider, so it is in their best interest to experiment with better methods. Kaiser Permanente implemented a pilot program in Hawaii for patients to engage in certain activities online—leveraging electronic records and substituting electronic interactions (secure messaging) for face-to-face office visits. The result was that primary care physician visits went down by 25.3 percent and customer satisfaction remained virtually unchanged, with 84 percent of members rating their overall satisfaction at eight or above on a 10-point scale in 2004 and 87 percent rating it at eight or above in 2007.[19] For Kaiser, these were great results, but for most physicians or health systems, these outcomes would decrease revenue because the current system is based upon volume, not value.

However, with changing consumer expectations, government legislation, and the general spotlight on reform, the tide is starting to change, and we are seeing the beginnings of supply-side innovation:

- **New "market entrants"** including virtual care from American Well and new delivery channels such as retail clinics like CVS Minute Clinic;
- **Self-service kiosks** at organizations like Kaiser to speed up registration and gather updated patient information to take the burden off healthcare professionals;[20]
- **Electronic personal health management platforms** like Microsoft HealthVault and Google Health; and,
- **"All-you-can-eat" subscription healthcare** ("concierge medicine") from organizations like Qliance, which eliminate insurance and deliver more primary care for fewer dollars.

Yet widespread change has not happened, as innovators are busy trying to bolt things onto the existing system rather than creating transformative solutions that we see in other competitive marketplaces like the cash-based systems of veterinary medicine, dentistry, or cosmetic surgery. For example, veterinarians offer e-mail or telephone consultations, make house calls, maintain electronic medical records, and so on, and pet owners willingly pay for these services. Veterinarians compete on price and quality, so they are constantly looking for innovations that allow them to provide better service and improve customer satisfaction. Because technology is often a source of innovation, they are quick to embrace new technologies that fuel better service and better patient care. We need to learn from this kind of model.

Furthermore, we are seeing innovations in other countries that we could implement ourselves. Entrepreneurs in countries like China and India have found ways to provide products and services at greatly reduced costs by reengineering the solutions to problems.[21] In India, for example, heart monitors and baby warmers have been redesigned so they cost 10 percent of what they do elsewhere, and small maternity hospitals cut costs to one-fifth of the price of services at larger private hospitals by outsourcing laboratory tests and pharmacy services.[22] The skeptics might say that quality will be sacrificed, but history has shown us how new market entrants have innovated and completely disrupted existing providers and entire industries.

Shift the Value Chain
Patients complain they are paying too much while doctors complain they are being paid too little.[23-24] They are both right. We need to let consumers and other health professionals like nurse practitioners or even software do some of the work that the most costly physicians should not and cannot be doing anymore. Physicians should be focused on using their unique expertise on the things that require very specialized knowledge and skills, like treating top-priority, chronic diseases.

Ten years ago, we would not have imagined that consumers would do so many things themselves. Technology and business model innovations have removed travel agents, bank tellers, and retailers as middlemen, and enabled all kinds of new services to be used through our phones and PCs. When we want to make a decision on what to buy, where to buy, whom to hire, or where to go, we have a nearly unlimited supply of resources to leverage to get informed before we act. Think of the possibilities for this kind of change in health.

A great example is the Mayo Clinic Health Manager, an online, interactive tool for families to manage their health data and seek personalized health guidance. Released in April of 2009, the Mayo Clinic Health Manager allows families to organize and store health information from a variety of sources (providers, devices, pharmacies, and health plans) in one location. This native HealthVault application applies a set of rules or protocols to the language of medicine and personal health information and delivers individualized health guidance from the Mayo Clinic with relevant tools and trackers that better inform patients. And since it is built on HealthVault, the data can be shared with the many other HealthVault applications, like the American Health Association's Heart360, helping consumers engage around specific needs for their personal conditions.

We are starting to see this kind of consumer self-serve shift occurring across healthcare with the advent of self-testing kits, such as for pregnancy, urinary tract infections, HIV, and hepatitis, as well as the move from expensive prescriptions to over-the-counter medicines.

Create a Technology Infrastructure to Drive the Benefits of Real-Time Data
At the foundation of all these recommendations is that healthcare IT must deliver the same real-time, real-life data upon which every other industry in America—from sports to transportation to mobile devices—runs.[25-27] To enable a patient-centric, scalable health system, the "right" information technology and infrastructure around data must be in place—software and services that connect consumers, providers, researchers, and sponsors of care to facilitate better outcomes. Traditionally, health data has been created for a single purpose, stuck in siloed systems, and discarded or archived when its purpose was complete. Data needs to be separated from applications and be stored so it can be repurposed and reused throughout a patient's life.[28] Health data will drive an efficient, high-quality, value-based, evidence-focused future for medicine, making it more of a science and less of an art.

An example of how this is coming to life is the Wisconsin Health Information Exchange (WHIE), a connected health infrastructure enabling the seamless flow of data. The project uses Microsoft Amalga to aggregate patient data from the state Medicaid claims system, 22 area hospitals, and more than 120 hospital-associated clinics and community health centers in southeast Wisconsin. Clinicians can access a patient's pharmacy prescription data, allergies, procedures, current and previous diagnoses, as well as hospital admission, discharge, and transfer records. They can see which tests have already been completed so they are not repeated. They can see if patients have been to the ER multiple times, so they can follow up more aggressively or put patients on a different care routine. The result? Better decisions in time-critical situations, reduced errors, and more effective care. The early success of the WHIE has prompted Humana, one of the nation's largest health benefits companies, to incentivize providers to utilize the WHIE system during the care process. In this program, Humana recognizes the value of applying health information exchange technology and its impact on avoiding duplication of services, and has agreed to provide a WHIE-administered incentive to ER physicians for utilization of the tool.

Another example is New York-Presbyterian Hospital (NYP), which has focused on creating a patient-centric approach by connecting the fragmented health ecosystem on several different levels. First, the hospital created a unified patient discharge report, which pulls data such as accompanying results (e.g., EKG), discharge medications, lab test results, clinical reports, operative reports, discharge summary, and discharge instructions from more than 56 data feeds from a myriad of NYP systems. NYP then enabled this discharge report to be accessed and stored by patients via a patient portal, myNYP.org. Patients can use HealthVault to share their data with their primary care physicians and broader care teams, or use it with a variety of personal health and wellness applications to manage their health in a more effective way. NYP has taken connectivity to another level by facilitating the automatic transfer of these reports (with patient consent) to their referral clinics or physicians (those who referred the patient to NYP in the first place) and vice versa.

Key to this process of data transfer is that the patient grants permission to the primary care physician and to NYP to look for and issue discharge reports. It is this one-time patient permission that allows the automated flow of data between NYP and outside medical groups. And most important, the data flows out of NYP discharge and into the existing EHR document queue at the referring physician's desk so that physician workflow is not negatively affected in any way. In fact, the physician has more information to better inform his or her own care when the patient follows up.

NYP is truly providing a seamless flow of information centered on the patient. These connections are already improving service and satisfaction, and are expected to improve health outcomes.

Unfortunately, most hospitals and other health stakeholders have been reluctant to embrace this type of technology. Whether it is because of the associated cost, the perceived complexity of such a solution, or a fear that they will adopt technology only to see it become outdated as soon as it is installed, the fact remains that healthcare providers and other key players have been reticent to adopt the changes that will move products and services in a new direction.

However, in 2009, Congress took the first step forward when it passed the *American Recovery and Reinvestment Act of 2009*, an economic stimulus package that included, among other things, $36 billion in funding to provide incentive payments to health care providers and organizations, encouraging them to adopt technology. For the first time, the proposed rule-making around "meaningful use" put a stake in the ground with real "sticks" and "carrots," describing the ideal state for strategic IT roadmaps as well as specific completion time frames. It actually attempts to describe technology as a means to improve health outcomes through real-time quality reporting, real-time data, connecting care across the continuum for patients and families. While there is a long road ahead, this legislation is a significant milestone in putting the foundational drivers for change in place.

This is important not only for today, but also for the future. We are on the cusp of amazing advancements with genomics and personalized medicine, which will bring exponential increases in the amount of data, personalized treatments, and decisions individuals can make. We need to ensure that we have the right technology foundation in place to support a completely new way of "doing it," one that we may not even be able to imagine today.

Building for the Future

At its heart, the United States is a country of innovators—great minds with even greater aspirations. Historically, we have led the globe with advancements and ideas that have transformed industries, from mobile innovations to computers to the latest medical devices and diagnostics. Things like government price setting and burdensome regulations have inhibited the natural innovation and world-class ideas for which the United States is known.

If we are to truly improve healthcare for our generation and those to come, we need to create the right kind of environment that will allow innovation to flourish. It is innovation that allows us to provide consumers with better care. It is innovation that empowers physicians with the knowledge of what works and what does not. And it is innovation that allows us to get more for every dollar invested in research. This is our opportunity to continue our legacy as a nation of innovators who export our knowledge of medicine to improve health around the world.

Peter Neupert is the Corporate Vice President in charge of the Health Solutions Group at Microsoft. In his position, Mr. Neupert works closely with the Chief Research and Strategy Officer and is responsible for driving the company's global product and services strategy for health—specifically identifying market opportunities and investments where Microsoft can provide software innovations that empower users and enable transformation to improve health in developed and developing economies.

[1] Microsoft Health Solutions Group, http://www.microsoft.com/hsg/ (accessed January 21, 2010).

[2] The Merck Institute for Science Education, "A Decade of Advances in Medicine 1993-2000," http://www.mise.org/mise/index.jsp?p=decade_home (accessed January 20, 2010).

[3] Umair Haque, "How to Think Constructively About Healthcare," *The Harvard Business Review Blog*, August 5, 2009, http://blogs.harvardbusiness.org/haque/2009/08/how_to_think_constructively_ab.html.

[4] Clayton M. Christensen, Jason Hwang, and Jerome H. Grossman, *The Innovator's Prescription* (New York: McGraw-Hill, 2008).

[5] Ibid., 47.

[6] Ibid., 47.

[7] Ibid., 47.

[8] "Chronic diseases account for 70% of leading causes of death in USA," *Medical News Today*, September 11, 2004, http:// www.medicalnewstoday.com/articles/13255.php.

[9] Centers for Disease Control and Prevention, "Chronic Diseases: The Power to Prevent, the Call to Control: At a Glance 2009," http://www.cdc.gov/chronicdisease/resources/publications/AAG/chronic.htm (accessed January 20, 2010).

[10] Ibid.

[11] Obesity Takes 9% of Health Spending," *CBS News*, July 27 2009, http://www.cbsnews.com/stories/2009/07/27/health/main5190909.shtml.

[12] Janet Rae-Dupree, "Unboxed: Disruptive Innovation, Applied to Health Care," *New York Times*, February 1, 2009, http://www.nytimes.com/2009/02/01/business/01unbox.html?_r=1.

[13] Joslin Diabetes Center, "An Overview of Diabetes," http://www.joslin.org/info/an_overview_of_diabetes.html.

[14] Darren Cason, "Banking Statistics Online," PopularArticles.com, September 11, 2009, http://www.populararticles.com/article173095.html.

[15] Danielle Belopotosky, "Marathon Tech: Rooting for Runners on Nov. 1," *New York Times*, October 26, 2009, http://gadgetwise.blogs.nytimes.com/2009/10/26/marathon-tech-a-guide-for-keeping-up-with-runners-on-nov-1/.

[16] Christensen, Hwang, and Grossman, *The Innovator's Prescription*.

[17] Rae-Dupree, "Unboxed: Disruptive Innovation, Applied to Health Care."

[18] Ibid.

[19] Catherine Chen, Terhilda Garrido, Don Chock, Grant Okawa, and Louise Liang, "Kaiser Permanente Electronic Health Record: Transforming and Streamlining Modalities of Care," *Health Affairs* 28.2 (2009): 324-33.

[20] Eric Wicklund, "Patients are keen on self-service healthcare," *Healthcare IT News*, http://www.healthcareitnews.com/news/patients-are-keen-self-service-healthcare.

[21] Eric Bellman, "Indian Firms Shift Focus to the Poor," *Wall Street Journal*, October 21, 2009, http://online.wsj.com/article/SB125598988906795035.html.

[22] "Lessons from a frugal innovator," *The Economist*, April 16, 2009, http://www.mim.monitor.com/downloads/Economist-LessonsfromaFrugalInnovator.pdf.

[23] Chen, et al., "Kaiser Permanente Electronic Health Record: Transforming and Streamlining Modalities of Care," *Health Affairs* 28, no. 2 (2009): 323-333.

[24] Uwe E. Reinhardt, "What Is a 'Just' Physician's Income?" *New York Times*, July 17, 2009, http://economix.blogs.nytimes.com/2009/07/17/what-is-a-just-physician-income/.

[25] Danielle Belopotosky, "Marathon Tech: Rooting for Runners on Nov. 1," *New York Times*, October 26, 2009, http://gadgetwise.blogs.nytimes.com/2009/10/26/marathon-tech-a-guide-for-keeping-up-with-runners-on-nov-1/.

[26] Jenna Wortham and Miguel Helft, "Hurting Rivals, Google Unveils Free Phone GPS," New York Times, October 29 2009, http://www.nytimes.com/2009/10/29/technology/companies/29gps.html.

[27] Rachel Metz, "Review: Motorola's Cliq Is A Snappy Smart Phone," *ABC News*, October 21, 2009, http://abcnews.go.com/Technology/wireStory?id=8881950.

[28] William W. Stead and Herbert S. Lin, eds. *Computational Technology for Effective Health Care: Immediate Steps and Strategic Directions* (Washington, D.C.: National Academies Press, 2009), 12.

CHAPTER 2

The Intermountain Blueprint
for Low-Cost, High-Quality Care

Brent James, M.D., Marc Probst, and Brandon Savage, M.D.

—ɷ—

Editor's Introduction

When people look for models of success that save lives and save money, they inevitably end up in the same place: Intermountain Healthcare in Utah. From evidence-based medicine and world-class outcomes to lower costs and patient engagement, Intermountain is a glimpse of what the rest of American healthcare could be. Its foundation has long been health information technology. Working closely with GE, Intermountain is creating exciting new technologies to meet the ever-growing demands of the 21st century. By exploring what they have accomplished, how they are doing it, and why they have done it, others can and should embrace these innovations for the benefit of all Americans. That is how we will transform our health system: seeking out what works and then actively designing policy to accelerate their adoption nationwide. There is no better place to start than Intermountain Healthcare.

—ɷ—

The *New York Times* Magazine recently published a feature article that pointed to the success of Intermountain Healthcare and held its model as a way to improve the quality of care delivered by healthcare organizations nationwide. The *Times* wrote, "The evidence-based medicine practiced at Intermountain hospital in Utah trades doctor's intuition for protocols in three-ring binders. It also seems to be saving lives."[1]

President Barack Obama has also cited Intermountain's good work. During an August 2009 speech to a Wisconsin audience, the president remarked:

> Even within our own country, a lot of the places where we
> spend less on healthcare actually have higher quality than

places where we spend more. We have to ask why places
like the Geisinger Health system in rural Pennsylvania,
Intermountain Health in Salt Lake City, or communities
like Green Bay can offer high-quality care at costs well
below average, but other places in America can't. We need
to identify the best practices across the country, learn
from the success, and replicate that success elsewhere.[2]

We at Intermountain are glad that our successes are getting
noticed by politicians and the media. While we are happy to
receive the recognition, we are more energized about the potential domino effect. Intermountain is seeking new ways to share
our know-how with other healthcare organizations across the
country. Our mission is to dispel the commonly held myth that
low-cost, high-quality healthcare is not achievable.

Busting the Cost and Quality Myth

For generations, the American healthcare system has operated under
the assumption that more is better—delivering healthcare with a
seemingly unending number of tests and treatments. But a growing body of evidence shows that this is an erroneous assumption.

For example, the Mayo Health Clinic in Rochester, Minnesota—long
cited as one of the nation's top clinical care providers—routinely
provides high-quality services at low costs. Mayo has been named
as a best hospital by *U.S. News & World Report* for 20 straight years,
and the *Dartmouth Atlas* confirms that Mayo uses fewer resources
and spends less per capita than its peers "while simultaneously
receiving high marks on established quality measures."[3]

Consider the following: A *Dartmouth* report says it cost Mayo's
Saint Mary's Hospital $34,372 to treat Medicare patients during
the final two years of life, whereas it costs their counterparts at a
leading West Coast hospital more than double: $71,637.[4]

Intermountain has been producing similar results that dispel
the high-spending, high-quality myth. A 2008 *Dartmouth* report
points out that Intermountain has driven down unnecessary
"supply sensitive care," or care that tends to be provided simply

because hospital beds, doctors, and specialized equipment are abundant, rather than because a patient clearly needs them. Using Intermountain as a benchmark, the 2008 *Dartmouth* report says the nation could reduce healthcare spending on acute and chronic illnesses by as much as 40 percent.[5]

The Groundwork

To accomplish all this, of course, would require change. The following changes are not easy, but they are essential to improve quality and lower costs.

Create Standards to Decrease Variability
Currently, healthcare is delivered without an empirical under-standing of outcomes and costs. Doctors, for example, make most of their diagnoses and treatment plans based on their experience and their current understanding of the clinical research. Simply keeping up with current medical knowledge is a Herculean task, as the growth of medical knowledge is estimated to double every 18 months to two years. As such, there is a great deal of unneces-sary variability inherent in how physicians deliver care and services.

Driving this unnecessary variation out of the process, however, can help to improve outcomes while reducing costs. If physi-cians know what standard of care has proven most clinically effective at the onset of each patient encounter, then physicians can more efficiently develop a treatment plan for each patient. As variation is reduced by providing standard baselines for treatment, physicians become free to focus their attentions on the unique attributes of each case and to tailor care to best meet the needs of the patient.

For instance, physicians typically prescribe medications based on their understanding of the current literature and what their personal experience tells them is an effective treatment. Much of the time these decisions are not based on real analysis or evi-dence of outcomes. However, if all physicians could start with a standard baseline that provides them with knowledge about the most effective medications at the lowest price for the majority of patients, healthcare organizations would drive costs down, while still enabling physicians to adapt all available evidence-based knowledge to the unique needs of each patient.

Providing preventive care to patients is also highly variable. For example, one physician might see patients older than 40 years for annual physical examinations, while another physician might see patients in this same age category every two years. Standards that spell out the most cost-effective interval for physical examinations could help to create more effective care as well.

Choose the Right Targets
Creating random standards of care, however, will not bring about the cost and quality advantages. Since only a handful of diseases are responsible for the majority of costs, organizations need to know where the biggest quality and cost advantages can be found. For example, will an organization get more for its efforts if clinical leaders develop standards for pediatric immunizations or anticoagulation or even hip replacements? The number of children who need pediatric immunization is far greater than the number of patients who need anticoagulation or hip replacements. Therefore, pediatric immunization standards are likely to drive more significant overall cost savings.

Change Work Processes
Typically, workflow processes in an institution simply develop as the culture evolves. The problem is that organizations are not keenly focused on performance improvement. Analyzing workflow, implementing innovations, and assessing results can, in fact, help organizations create work processes that are much more effective than what is in place. In addition, organizations can improve performance by assigning specific professionals to specific tasks. For example, it could benefit an organization if nurse managers could manage the predictable and recurring preventive care or chronic disease needs for a patient while physicians tailor the care and plans for further diagnostics.

Optimize and Sustain Overall Performance

The changes mentioned above are critical to becoming a high-performing organization, but leaders also need to know the key

improve care, not withhold it. Though most providers do not currently have the same financial incentives in place, and therefore do not directly benefit from providing cost-efficient care, Intermountain's experience proves that care can improve significantly when costs incentives are aligned accordingly.

With the organization's culture and payment model setting the stage, Intermountain has been able to find the right formula to deliver high-value care while lowering costs.

Learning from Deming
About 30 years ago, Intermountain adopted many of the philosophies of W. Edwards Deming, the quality improvement pioneer who is credited with revolutionizing manufacturing, most notably through his work with the Japanese auto industry. The process began with a series of studies to measure variations in care delivery that were based on Deming's quality improvement theory. Intermountain embraced the philosophy that by improving the outcomes of clinical processes, the cost of operations would drop.

An essential element of Deming's approach is to analyze and eliminate variability. By sharing findings about variability and best practices, practice patterns began to shift as physicians quickly learned from each other.

Additionally, after an intense analysis that identified and prioritized the clinical conditions that make up the workflow processes, Intermountain realized that of approximately 1,400 clinical conditions, just 104 accounted for about 95 percent of the care delivered within the system. Specifically, labor and delivery totaled 11 percent of the system's work, and management of ischemic heart disease accounted for 10 percent. Intermountain zeroed in on these most common areas first. With a clearly defined focus, the organization developed standardized protocols that would guide clinicians to deliver the highest-quality, most cost-effective care for these two conditions.

A practice improvement course was developed that continued the variance analysis across multiple clinical programs and directly resulted in $30 million in annual savings. It was determined that broad adoption across the delivery system would eventually help Intermountain realize $150 million in annual savings.

Intermountain continually adds protocols to its system. Currently, about 80 percent of care delivery is evidence-based, as opposed to less than 55 percent for the rest of the industry.[6] These protocols, which start out as paper-based directives and eventually are rolled into Intermountain's clinical computing systems, are used as a "shared baseline" at the patient bedside. As such, physicians are expected to launch their treatments based on these protocols and make necessary adjustments to meet the individual needs of each patient.

The Information Technology Engine
Information technology is leveraged in two fundamental ways at Intermountain. First, information technology is the key to effectively implementing quality improvement initiatives. IT provides timely and accurate data about processes, costs, and outcomes, which is the heart of quality improvement. Intermountain has adopted many of the philosophies that have been implemented in the manufacturing industry such as LEAN, a quality-improvement practice that has gained widespread acceptance in a number of industries due to its initial success at Toyota. To successfully implement LEAN programs, information technology is used to automate processes, present complex data in easy-to-understand formats, and improve communication across the enterprise. The result is a streamlined process that eliminates waste.

Second, Intermountain is a leader in using information technology to support clinical care. Intermountain has had a fully operational electronic health record system since 1975. Developed in-house and considered one of the first electronic health records (EHR), it has produced many of the efficiency benefits associated with automating various processes. The technology was at the heart of the Deming-inspired analyses—from capturing the data to identifying priorities to changing processes.

However, Intermountain recently decided that in order to move forward with the development of even more robust evidence-based medicine, for its own organization and for the healthcare industry as a whole, it would need a system that goes well beyond simply automating paper-based processes.

A Partnership with GE
To take on this challenge, Intermountain found a valuable partner in GE. Together, Intermountain and GE are working to develop a true 21st-century system that helps clinicians deliver the best possible care at the bedside while simultaneously generating valuable data that can be analyzed to drive further improvements in the future. The technology will provide a standardized, portable representation of healthcare guidelines and best practices that can be leveraged by existing information technology applications such as electronic medical records.

The system will not simply make it easy for clinicians to input information and deliver high-quality care; it will also draw "intelligence" out of the system. Data can be analyzed to determine the most effective therapies and treatments, helping clinicians keep up with the constant creation of new medical knowledge. The system will be able to change clinical content within two to four days, instead of the two to four months that is typical. In an era of reform and ongoing change, institutions need this level of agility to adapt their practices and procedures to deliver the best care at the right cost.

To achieve high responsiveness, the system will work like a DVD player, where the content will be separated from the software that runs the system. Embedded into the software will be three decades' worth of clinical protocols developed at Intermountain. Clinicians will use the system to help guide their care delivery using whatever evidence-based protocol they need for the specific patient they are treating, from labor and delivery to chronic-care management. They can plug in their own patient data and use tailored, evidence-based treatment on their specific patients. The system also aggregates the new information that is generated, so any user of the system can contribute to this growing body of protocols, making it possible to quickly expand the body of evidence-based intelligence that organizations can use.

The solution will offer a series of financial reports that provide information at the system level right down to the physician and

the many problems inherent in the nation's health system to the high-quality clinical results possible through evidence-based medicine. Organizations will be able to define what is important to them and then measure the gap between their ultimate goals and their current practices. From there, leaders can leverage data to map and implement new workflows and provide decision support. After measuring their success, they can then make additional changes to further optimize performance. This constant circle of performance improvement may just be what is needed to finally help the healthcare industry achieve the successes that have been realized in other industries, and to move toward a model of care that integrates clinical and financial decision-making while improving patient outcomes.

—∞—

Brent James, M.D. is the Chief Quality Officer and Executive Director of the Institute for Health Care Delivery Research at Intermountain Healthcare, based in Salt Lake City, Utah. Intermountain is an integrated system of 22 hospitals, almost 140 clinics, a 700+ member physician group, and an HMO/PPO insurance plan jointly responsible for more than 500,000 covered lives, serving patients in Utah, Idaho, and seven surrounding states. Through the Intermountain Advanced Training Program in Clinical Practice Improvement, Dr. James has trained more than 3,500 worldwide senior physician, nursing, and administrative executives in clinical management methods.

Marc Probst is the Chief Information Officer and Vice President at Intermountain Healthcare. Mr. Probst has been a leader in information technology and healthcare services for the past 18 years and has been appointed to serve on the Federal Healthcare Information Technology Policy Committee, which is assisting in developing HIT policy for the U.S. government.

Brandon Savage, M.D. is Chief Medical Officer and General Manger of Global Marketing for GE Healthcare's Integrated IT Solutions business. His responsibilities include working with the healthcare community to establish GE's healthcare IT vision and driving requirements into current and future products that enable digital communities and early health. At GE, Dr. Savage has led the development of products such as computerized provider order entry and other software applications focused on knowledge management, collaborative workflow, and decision support.

—⚏—

[1] David Leonhardt, "Making Health Care Better," *New York Times Magazine*, November 3, 2009, http://www.nytimes.com/2009/11/08/magazine/08Healthcare-t.html.

[2] Bernie Monegain, "Intermountain, Geisinger Share the Spotlight in Obama Talk," *Healthcare IT News*, June 12, 2009, http://www.healthcareitnews.com/news/intermountain-geisingershare-spotlight-obama-talk.

[3] "Tracking the Care of Patients with Severe Chronic Illness: *Dartmouth Medical Atlas of 2008*," *Dartmouth Institute for Health Policy and Clinical Practice*, http://www.dartmouthatlas.org/atlases/2008_Chronic_Care_Atlas.pdf.

[4] Jeff Hansel, "Healthcare at the Mayo Clinic: High Quality, Low Cost," *Post-Bulletin*, July 25, 2009.

[5] J. Wennberg, MD, E. Fisher, MD, et al., "An Agenda for Change: A Dartmouth Atlas White Paper," *Dartmouth Institute for Health Policy and Clinical Practice*, http://www.dartmouthatlas.org/topics/agenda_for_change.pdf.

[6] Paul Shekelle, Margaret Maglione, and Sally Morton, "Preponderance of evidence: Judging what to do about Ephedra," *Rand Review: Spring 2003*, http://www.rand.org/publications/randreview/issues/spring2003/evidence.html.

[7] First Consulting Group, "Centricity Product Value Analysis," http://www.csc.com/ (accessed January 21, 2010).

[8] PriceWaterhouseCoopers, "Rock and a hard place: An analysis of the $36 billion impact from health IT stimulus funding," http://www.pwc.com/us/en/healthcare/publications/rock-and-ahard-place.jhtml, (accessed January 15, 2010).

CHAPTER 3

The Progress and Potential of Patient-Centered Medical Homes

Sarah T. Corley, M.D., F.A.C.P., and Charles W. Jarvis, F.A.C.H.E.

—꘠—

Editor's Introduction

If the U.S. healthcare system were a business, it would have filed for bankruptcy long ago. No company could survive by offering its customers skyrocketing prices, poor quality, and limited access. However, that is exactly what we get in healthcare today. We need dramatic change. And the patient-centered medical home is a vital part of the solution. This approach strengthens the doctor-patient relationship, focuses on health not just illness, and overcomes one of the most inefficient and deadly aspects of the current system: the fragmentation of care, where treatment occurs in isolation with virtually no information about a patient's past. Tools like electronic health records are the foundation of a medical home because they allow primary care physicians to connect with other stakeholders in the system, share information, and better coordinate the delivery of care. While adoption of the medical home model is far from universal, there are pioneers that have demonstrated its transformational potential.

—꘠—

Just over a decade ago, the Institute of Medicine (IOM) released the groundbreaking publication, *To Err Is Human: Building a Safer Health System*, which revealed the staggering consequences of medical errors in U.S. hospitals: an annual cost of as much as $29 billion and at least 44,000 deaths—perhaps as many as 98,000—attributed directly to those medical errors.[1] The IOM commented, "When patients see multiple providers in different settings, none of whom has access to complete information, it becomes easier for things to go wrong."

More recently, a November 2008 white paper issued by Senate Finance Committee chairman Max Baucus (D-MT) again spelled out the clinical and business toll exacted by the current system of care.[2] It noted that 45 percent of Americans suffer from one or more chronic conditions, such as heart disease, stroke, cancer, and diabetes. Chronic disease accounts for 70 percent of the deaths in the United States, and "treatment of the seven most common chronic diseases, coupled with productivity losses, costs the U.S. economy more than $1 trillion annually. About 78 percent of the nation's total health care spending is due to chronic illness."[3]

These and other measurements have caused the United States to fall far short of being the healthiest society in the world, despite spending one-sixth of our entire gross domestic product on healthcare. One reason is that we spend the vast majority of our resources treating the symptoms of disease rather than treating the causes. People seek fragmented, acute-based care when they need it, and physicians are paid when they treat the sick, not when they prevent illness.

The conclusion drawn by many clinicians and economists alike was succinctly stated in the Baucus paper: "Prevention must become a cornerstone of the healthcare system rather than an afterthought."[4] However, this will require a fundamental shift toward placing a premium on broad-spectrum coordination of information and clinical resources that promote health, rather than simply treat illness.

There is a model of care that can accomplish all this: the patient-centered medical home (PCMH). It is a care environment based on evidence, driven by data, focused on wellness, and centered on the needs of the patient. This approach can help drive a healthier America, with fewer errors and less strain on our limited resources. Many forward-thinking organizations already have adopted this care model and discovered its benefits. Some have advanced even further, rising to the level of a technology-based PCMH with results that are path-breaking.

What Is the Patient-Centered Medical Home?

Any explanation of the PCMH must begin by clarifying what it is not. Many mistakenly associate it with a physical location, such as a nursing home or an assisted living center, when, in fact, the opposite is true. The medical "home" is a team-based, virtual network of doctors, nurses, and other providers that share information about the patient to coordinate his or her medical care better.

The PCMH emphasizes and requires the patient and his or her primary care provider to work as a team that shares responsibility for the patient's care. That responsibility includes not only providing care, but also coordinating it system-wide, with specialists and other ancillary care providers as needed. The patient and primary care physician are at the hub of the decision-making wheel, with other medical services and providers—such as hospitals, home health, and pharmacists—as its supporting spokes.

Key Characteristics

In 2007, the American Academy of Family Physicians, the American Academy of Pediatrics, the American College of Physicians, and the American Osteopathic Association published the "Joint Principles of the Patient-Centered Medical Home" to outline key characteristics of a PCMH:[5]

- **Whole-person orientation**: The primary care physician is responsible for meeting all of the patient's healthcare needs or arranging appropriate care with other qualified professionals. This includes care for all stages of life: acute care, chronic care, preventive services, and end-of-life care.

- **Care coordination:** Care is integrated across all elements of the healthcare system and the patient's community to ensure that patients get the indicated care when and where they need and want it, and in a culturally and linguistically appropriate manner.

- **Quality and safety measurements:** Care is based on evidence and best practices, using clinical decision-support tools to guide decision-making. Physicians accept accountability for continuous quality improvement through voluntary engagement in performance measurement. Information technology is utilized appropriately to support optimal patient care, performance measurement, patient education, and enhanced communication.

- **Payment:** Provider reimbursement complements the additional responsibility and is properly aligned to reflect the benefits of the medical home and the additional value providers contribute.

- **Enhanced access**: Care is improved through enhancements such as open scheduling, expanded hours, and new options for communication between patients and the primary care team.

Many primary care practices today have implemented this model and documented improvements in care delivery and quality. They have often been in partnership with hospitals and private insurers. While some of these practices still work from a paper-based foundation, those that have embraced health information technology (HIT) have seen better results compared to their paper-based PCMH counterparts.

"Just as pen and paper were 20th-century methods for practicing medicine, giving attention to the patient only when he/she is in your office is an outdated method of healthcare delivery," according to Dr. James L. Holly, CEO of the multi-specialty group SouthEast Texas Medical Associates (SETMA) in Beaumont, Texas, who has been practicing this method of care delivery in an automated setting for several years.

One approach made possible in an automated PCMH model is to provide electronic visits, or e-visits. The Medical College of Wisconsin family medicine residencies, for example, have created a web-based portal for patient messaging, scheduling, education, and communication of test results. A secure Internet portal allows communication about non-urgent issues, with staff committed to responding within a single business day, according to Program Administrator Sandra Olsen, MS, BA.

Elmhurst Clinic in Elmhurst, Illinois, is part of a Blue Cross Blue Shield medical home pilot that offers patients a secure, integrated

Internet portal to request appointments or medication refills and access to their medication lists, lab, and diagnostic test results. This can be done through any Internet connection or even on a cell phone. All communication is documented in Elmhurst's EHR system.

New Pueblo Medicine in Tucson, Arizona, uses technology to enhance the patient experience by tracking response time to patient calls. Call reports are linked to same-day scheduling, giving patients faster responses and more convenience, notes CEO Michael Cracovaner.

The Medical Clinic of North Texas in Dallas/Ft. Worth uses an interface between its EHR system and a clinical protocol engine to automatically generate a personalized "patient recommendation report" for every patient at every visit, regardless of the reason for the visit, according to Chief Administrative Officer Karen Kennedy. That means each provider has appropriate, patient-specific clinical protocols available to reference and act upon during every patient exam, ensuring all conditions and disease states are being effectively managed. As a result of such proactive measures, the Medical Clinic of North Texas can demonstrate clinical improvements such as:

- Diabetic patients with a current HgA1c increased from 40 percent to 88 percent;
- Patients with a current LDL increased from 24 percent to 67 percent;
- Female patients who had current cervical cancer screening increased from 45 percent to 63 percent;
- Patients who had current mammograms increased from 38 percent to 59 percent; and,
- Diabetic patients who had an annual foot exam increased from 5 percent to 45 percent.

HIT is the information centerpiece of all these successes.

Electronic Data Capture and Exchange: Both Breakthrough and Barrier

What sets the patient-centered medical home apart from other care models? Dr. Holly of SETMA notes that "the 'connector' for all of the elements of care which we are doing is the medical home care coordination database and review."[6]

Indeed, the critical difference between the PCMH and a typical acute-based, fragmented approach is data management. The automated medical home has been called "high touch/high tech" care. The "high touch" is the desire of the care providers to work in concert with one another as members of a care team; "high tech" is technology integration that allows patients to see multiple providers in different settings, all of whom have electronic access to a current, complete record of patient health information. The proactive use of electronic tools to manage patient data and drive decision-making is essential.

Capturing and exchanging electronic patient data lies at the heart of this collaborative approach, as the model cannot exist without it. The current paper-based approach cannot provide the requisite data interconnectivity, accessibility, tracking, reporting, and analytic functions to allow a primary-care team to build a true medical home. In fact, one of the largest obstacles to widespread adoption of the medical home model is a lack of information technology use to capture and exchange data.

With healthcare IT adoption rates still unacceptably low, the ability to achieve widespread adoption of this model is going to be limited. It will take a concerted commitment to and acceptance of IT before we begin to realize the gains that this enhanced data management can bring.

Models of Success

WellStar Health System
WellStar Health System in Atlanta, Georgia, has realized many of the core benefits of the PCMH model in its automated practices. Dr. Marcia Delk, WellStar's Senior Vice President for Medical Affairs and Chief Quality Officer, notes significant administrative savings. A pilot cost comparison conducted by WellStar showed that the group was spending $24,885 in administrative costs to conduct manual quality review of 30 charts per physician for the NCQA Diabetes Provider Recognition program. By comparison,

the same review cost $156.25 when WellStar performed it using an EHR system.

The clinical gains are equally striking. Take, for example, blood pressure management in diabetic patients. One of the care metrics being tracked in the WellStar PCMH program is the number of diabetic patients who attain good blood pressure control, defined as systolic pressure below 130 and diastolic pressure below or equal to 80. Since tracking began, WellStar has seen the percentage of patients meeting the goal rise from 33 percent to 60 percent, while those with readings above 140/90—considered not meeting their care goal—dropped from 25 percent to 21 percent.

Community Health Centers
Community health centers (CHCs) in particular, where HIT adoption rates are much higher than in private practice, have helped develop the medical home model by focusing on team-based primary care, prevention, and coordination, the core of their organizational structure. Through the use of EHR systems, community health centers have helped patients avoid emergency rooms and make better use of preventive services, in turn saving more than $17 billion a year, according to the National Association of Community Health Centers.[7]

One successful example comes from CHC Collaborative Ventures in Arizona, a group that supports 12 federally qualified health center organizations. The practices within Collaborative Ventures utilize practice management and EHR systems, which facilitate the sharing of patient medical information among primary- and specialty-care practices. Since deployment of the EHR systems in January 2008, improved reporting capabilities and access to comprehensive patient data have given participating providers the ability to monitor long-term trends in patient outcomes. Midway through 2009, 80 percent of providers had adopted the EHR technology, utilizing IT tools that allow them to better gauge the impact of their disease management programs on their patient populations. As progress continues in upcoming months, the providers will be able to aggregate the data to conduct meaningful peer-based outcome reporting. Over the longer term, participants plan to implement a community health solution technology, enabling them to create a statewide CHC network capable of data-sharing and improved population management.

The NCQA Approach

The non-profit National Committee for Quality Assurance (NCQA) has championed the cause of improving healthcare quality for two decades. Already known for a wide variety of healthcare accreditation, certification, and recognition programs, NCQA now offers practices the chance to attain its Physician Practice Connections® –Patient-Centered Medical Home™ (PPC–PCMH) Recognition.

PPC-PCMH builds on the joint principles noted above to provide recognition for practices that establish "systematic, patient-centered, coordinated care management processes."[8] The organization created nine standards for certification that encompass 30 elements and 189 data points, including care management, patient self-management support, electronic prescribing, performance reporting and improvement, and advanced electronic communications.

Practices can receive one of three levels of recognition as PCMHs, depending on their mastery of the standards. Crystal Run Healthcare, a 200+ provider multi-specialty group practice in New York, for example, has received Level-3 recognition, the highest possible. It attributes its success to the detailed patient knowledge it collects, manages, and shares through an integrated EHR system. For instance, the group's lab and radiology information systems import clinical data directly into patient charts, giving clinicians easy, point-of-care access at all locations. Physicians can take laptops from room to room or building to building. On-call staff can log in from anywhere—home, office, hospital, or elsewhere—via a secure virtual private network to access patient information.

The EHR system and messaging of clinical information is tightly integrated across the Crystal Run enterprise. Clinical systems are also meshed with communication services, as the practice adopted the BlackBerry platform several years ago to more seamlessly communicate. Laboratory and radiology turnaround times, as well as reporting of critical results, are also closely tracked.

Crystal Run's results include 93 percent of radiology reports now available and delivered to the ordering provider within 24 hours, and 98 percent of International Normalized Ratios (to report anti-coagulation level) reported within one hour of being obtained. The practice has also installed a centralized call center to handle 4,000 calls a day, capture information, and forward it to the appropriate physician via e-mail, who then records outcomes in the EHR system.

The Gilbert Center for Family Medicine in Gilbert, Arizona, has also earned Level-3 PCMH recognition. According to Practice Manager Jim Stape, Gilbert's automated interfaces with several lab and radiology facilities, e-mail notification of emergency department visits and in-patient admissions, and detailed reporting on evidence-based practices, coupled with patient compliance, all contributed to the recognition. While measurable cost reduction has not been published yet, pertinent clinical measures have shown excellent results. Measures such as HgA1c indicate 83 percent of Gilbert's total diabetic patient population is below 7.0.

SouthEast Texas Medical Associates
SouthEast Texas Medical Associates (SETMA) is pursuing Level-3 NCQA recognition as well, and will use its EHR system to better track and generate:

- Reports provided the day prior to a patient visit that detail what each patient needs during the next day's visit, including requirements to meet all quality measures the group is tracking;
- Performance results from the previous day's visits. The immediacy with which individual provider performance is measured against all SETMA providers is aimed at helping effect positive change more rapidly; and,
- Practice-wide performance information (without patient or provider identification), which will be posted on the SETMA public website. The goal is to bolster patient confidence in the standard of care, as well as motivate providers to continue raising that standard.

In the near future, it is expected that payers will begin to tie the levels of NCQA recognition for patient-centered medical homes to the amount of care management fee reimbursement they offer. Many major commercial payers, including United Healthcare, Aetna, CIGNA, WellPoint, and Kaiser, already are initiating PCMH pilot programs that incorporate standards from NCQA, or even require NCQA certification before offering incentive rewards.

Bridges to Excellence
Bridges to Excellence (BTE) is another not-for-profit collaboration that creates and implements care and reporting programs to help realign incentives around quality. Among its many objectives are driving the use of health IT by leveraging existing quality reporting/data aggregation initiatives and facilitating the connection between quality improvement and financial incentives.

For example, BTE accepts PPC-PCMH Recognition to satisfy the qualification requirements for its Physician Office Link rewards. In this program, physician offices qualify for bonus payments, which BTE negotiates with private insurers based on implementation of specific quality improvement and error reduction processes. A program "report card" is then made available for the public to review. While an EHR system in itself has not been a requirement for participation, successful tracking of quality improvement and error reduction initiatives is extremely difficult without one.

The automated PCMH model is an ideal fit for the BTE value system. "The proactive uses of technology to develop the patient-centered medical home fit nicely with the Bridges to Excellence core principles: transform care to reduce mistakes, reduce underuse, and increase quality improvements," notes Mary Stull, RN, PhD, Vice President and COO of the Elmhurst Clinic's physician practice division.

WellStar has also earned rewards through the BTE program and has achieved some major breakthroughs in automated care modeling in the last year. "We have been really pleased with the results of the BTE and (NextGen) EHR collaboration. As we expand the program, we know the thirteen physicians who received BTE incentives are just the beginning," notes Dr. Delk of WellStar.

Coordination of Care and Patient Engagement: Cornerstones of Quality

The PCMH is built on a close relationship between the primary care team and the patient, where sharing information and responsibility is a key to success. The more patients know about and understand their health, the more they can take responsibility for it. However, it also requires primary care physicians to gather and manage patient information and educate patients beyond isolated episodes of care. To accomplish this without automation is nearly impossible and increases the chances of inaccurate and inconsistent results between patient files and physician records.

Physicians at Crystal Run in New York, for example, have personalized the care they deliver by tapping into EHR data at the point of care to analyze patient status. Patients receive a heightened awareness of their health when, for instance, providers hand them a history of their own vital signs to show progress toward—or deviation from—their personalized care goals. In turn, this can increase patient compliance with care plans, particularly for improving chronic disease. "Our EHR gives us detailed knowledge of our patients, allowing us to improve care by moving patient data to the appropriate specialists," notes practicing partner Dr. Greg Spencer.

Patients identified as high-risk for certain conditions, or who are already struggling with them, are urged to enroll in appropriate disease management programs at Crystal Run. They are assigned a nurse who regularly reviews their medical records to assess risk factors and coordinate what care they should be utilizing. This approach has bumped mammography screening for breast cancer to an 82 percent compliance rate for patients in their care management program, well above the 72 percent national average reported by the NCQA.[9]

Elmhurst Clinic in Illinois employs an automated method for proactively contacting patients with chronic conditions due for follow-up appointments. Diagnostic data and visit histories from the group's practice management system are sent to an electronic program that uses evidence-based protocols to identify patients who are overdue for a visit. A series of reminder calls is generated for each patient, with a call history returned to Elmhurst's EHR for compliance tracking. During the first three quarters of 2009, Elmhurst booked over 7,000 appointments as a direct result of automated outreach. Over 2,000 of these visits pertained to the management of chronic conditions associated with the medical home.

"We look at the selection and development of our technology—and all of our processes—based on their ability to enhance our patients' experiences and keep them in the center of all we do," says Stull.

Widespread Adoption: Next Steps in the Process

A number of public- and private-sector programs aimed at testing the PCMH model currently exist. Late in 2009, for example, the Centers for Medicare and Medicaid Services announced it would partner with several multi-payer medical home pilots on a project titled the Multi-Payer Advanced Primary Care Practice Demonstration. More funding and pilots were included in several of the leading bills in Congress to overhaul the nation's health system, and indeed the federal government is "counting" on this effort to help achieve some of the savings needed to pay for the major investments being made to achieve health reform today. But bringing the medical home concept to fruition in a meaningful, broadly adoptable way requires five distinct actions:

1. **Understanding.** All parties—payer, patient, and clinician—must come to the realization that real transformation is essential. Providers, in particular, will need to adjust to a new model for both reimbursement and care delivery.
2. **Validation.** Adequate time must be spent obtaining and analyzing results from the various federal and private payer pilot projects now under way, so that any nationwide reform efforts rest on solid data.
3. **Commitment.** Government and commercial payers will need to reinforce their dedication to the concept by more openly promoting it.
4. **Education.** Patients must be educated regarding the value of the PCMH, and physicians must be taught how to derive the greatest clinical and business benefits from it.

5. **IT adoption.** The healthcare community must adopt and use information technology. Simply put, none of the responsive, proactive, data-intensive processes at the core of the medical home model is feasible in a cumbersome, labor-intensive, paper-based environment.

These are, admittedly, daunting tasks—especially when more than 75 percent of physician practices are still paper-based. But the impact of PCMH hinges on widespread implementation and use of information technology. Critical steps have been taken to make this a reality. Titles VIII and XIII of the *American Recovery and Reinvestment Act of 2009* will provide tens of billions of dollars in incentives and other funding over the next several years that will allow practices to transform themselves into patient-centered medical homes.

Conclusion

The IOM's conclusion that "things go wrong" without access to complete information would not be a valid criticism today if the patient-centered medical home were more prevalent. The tools exist now to give every provider and patient access to all information necessary to prevent errors, improve patient satisfaction, and improve quality outcomes. The physician practices identified in this chapter are all brilliant examples of what can happen when high-quality, well-intentioned providers adopt this model and use health information technology to maximize its benefits.

—⚏—

Sarah T. Corley, M.D., F.A.C.P., is the Chief Medical Officer of Next-Gen Healthcare Information Systems. NextGen is a full-service organization serving the needs of physician practices, hospitals, health centers, and other healthcare providers. Dr. Corley also continues to practice part-time as a primary care internist in the metropolitan Washington, D.C., area. She recently completed a four-year term as Governor of the Virginia Chapter of the American College of Physicians and a six-year term on its National Medical Informatics Subcommittee.

Charles W. Jarvis, F.A.C.H.E., is Vice President of Healthcare Services and Government Relations for NextGen Healthcare Information Systems.

Mr. Jarvis is responsible for community and partnership development, including oversight of the company's grants and client funding assistance program, clinical outcomes business planning, and government relations. He is also responsible for internal and external education on the evolution of the healthcare industry with a focus on healthcare information technology stimulus and health reform.

[1] Linda T. Kohn, Janet M. Corrigan, and Molla S. Donaldson, eds., *To Err Is Human: Building a Safer Health System* (Washington, D.C.: National Academy Press, 2000).
[2] "Call to Action: Health Reform 2009," U.S. Senate Finance Committee, November 12, 2008, http://finance.senate.gov/healthreform2009/finalwhitepaper.pdf.
[3] Ibid., 28.
[4] Ibid., 28.
[5] Patient-centered Primary Care Collaborative, "Joint Principles of the Patient-Centered Medical Home," February 2007, http://www.pcpcc.net/content/joint-principles-patientcentered-medical-home (accessed January 20, 2010).
[6] James L. Holly, M.D., "Medical Home Part X: A Summation of the Beginning of a Journey," *The Examiner* (Beaumont), June 4, 2009.
[7] National Association of Community Health Centers, "About Our Health Centers," http://www.nachc.org/about-our-health-centers.cfm (accessed January 20, 2010).
[8] National Committee for Quality Assurance, "PPC: Patient-Centered Medical Home," http://www.ncqa.org/tabid/631/default.aspx (accessed January 21, 2010).
[9] National Committee for Quality Assurance, "NCQA 2008 Quality Compass," http://www.ncqa.org/tabid/177/Default.aspx (accessed January 21, 2010).

CHAPTER 4

The Transformative Convergence
of Diagnostics and Health IT

Thomas J. Miller

—m—

Editor's Introduction

The future of healthcare is now. We can see it all around us, from the growth of genomics to brain sciences to breakthroughs in treating chronic disease. Just as bits of data are scattered across the system, what has been missing is the glue that binds together information and innovation. That is one of the most promising aspects of health information technology (HIT). Doctors, nurses, and other providers can access a comprehensive electronic medical record, where updated and accurate patient information can be securely stored and exchanged. That can be coupled with information from powerful new technologies like molecular imaging, breakthrough laboratory diagnostics, and other tools of personalized medicine. When all clinicians have accurate, reliable, and updated information from the most sophisticated devices and technologies available, patients will undoubtedly benefit and the system will be transformed.

—m—

There is now a perfect storm—a convergence of dynamics and technologies that can have a transformational effect on the application of healthcare and medicine. Spiraling costs, the essential driver of healthcare reform, and a sicker, aging population are fundamentally changing the approach to medicine and moving from a reactive "treat the sick" model to a proactive "protecting lifelong health" model.

In the United States, the clamor over reform has been as much about costs as it has been about access. Healthcare costs doubled from 1996 to 2006 and are projected to rise to 25 percent of GDP by 2025.[1] On top of this, we already spend twice the average of other developed countries. However, in analyzing trends, costs are rising for *all* industrialized nations, steadily climbing for almost 20 years. The United Kingdom, with its national socialized system, is experiencing an overall growth in healthcare spending—at a rate that is actually rising faster than costs in the United States.[2]

These economic pressures, combined with the specific reasons that are driving costs ever higher, highlight that our system is sick and demands that our approach must drastically change. Attempting to sustain the current model will result in financial ruin.

Drivers of Costs

Many analysts believe that innovations such as growth in drug development and in new medical technologies are major contributing factors in healthcare spending. Though pharmaceuticals do make up the fastest-growing segment of healthcare spending, the single largest source of spending comes from treating chronic diseases, which accounts for 75 percent of total healthcare costs and 81 percent of hospital admissions in the United States.[3] This is a by-product of a population that, while living longer, is also living with chronic diseases such as high blood pressure, diabetes, and cardiovascular disease. End-of-life care costs are also extraordinary. In 2008, Medicare paid $50 billion in physician and hospital bills for care during the last two months of patients' lives.[4]

Though chronic disease management is the largest contributor to healthcare spending, diagnosing and then treating an illness is also an expensive process. For all our medical advances, modern science does not hold all the answers. We often do not know why a drug will be effective for one patient and useless for another. This "trial and error" approach costs money and, more importantly, lives. Current estimates of overall drug effectiveness are disappointing, ranging from as low as 10 percent to as high as 50 percent.[5-6]

Knowledge Is Power: Personalized Medicine Is Practiced Today

Despite the cost factors facing the healthcare industry, we are living in a time when medicine is poised to make dramatic leaps forward. The rate of change in the advancement of clinical knowledge is astounding and presents an unprecedented opportunity to transform medicine. Such advances, including the ability to predict an individual's risk of developing a specific disease and knowledge of the disease itself at a molecular level (its unique attributes in that individual) dramatically alter how we approach and treat illness. Increasingly, innovations in in-vitro (laboratory testing) and in-vivo (medical imaging) diagnostics allow physicians to diagnose and characterize diseases earlier—a running head start that allows us to find and stop diseases before they reach catastrophic states.

Despite the new knowledge we have, adopting it into common practice is a challenge. Clinicians are, after all, still human and managing the expansion in knowledge is beyond the capacity of the human brain. On average, it is a full 17 years before new knowledge reaches a critical mass, i.e., in practice by half of all physicians.[7] Consider the example that only half of the 24 million Americans living with diabetes receive the appropriate, best practice standard of care.[8]

This lays much of the foundation for the federal government's drive to implement advanced healthcare information technology systems as a mechanism to control costs and improve quality. What is required are systems that provide a digital view of the individual's medical history—the electronic patient record—and that give access to the vast data warehouses of clinical knowledge that brings to bear on each individual's care.

For example, imagine if a patient presents at the emergency room with a suspected heart attack, Acute Coronary Syndrome (ACS). Typically, a physician would admit the patient for further observation and testing to rule out ACS at a cost in excess of $4,000. Now, suppose the physician reviewed the patient's electronic medical record and notes that there is not a history of cardiovascular disease. Next, the same HIT system alerts the physician to a new best practice protocol to consider for this patient. That protocol deems it safe and effective to perform a Cardiac Computed Tomography Angiography (CCTA) in the ER, with a laboratory test with a high sensitivity assay for cardiac troponin to diagnose and rule out a cardiac event. The time to diagnose or send the patient home is less than eight hours and costs approximately $1,500. Time, money, and precious hospital resources are spared.

Tangible examples of personalized medicine in practice are also found in our approaches to breast cancer. As our understanding of the disease has expanded, diagnosis and treatment paths have become more complex. Testing women for mutations in the BRCA 1 and 2 genes has become the standard predictive technique to assess increased risk for breast cancer. This knowledge has enabled thousands of women who test positively for the mutations to better understand that their risk of developing breast cancer is five times greater than a woman who does not have the mutation.[9] Women diagnosed with breast cancer that tests as positive for the HER2/neu gene are given a specific, targeted therapy of Herceptin, which specifically attacks HER2 and decreases the risk of recurrence.

Core to managing the care process for such a patient is HIT, which would alert the radiologist, while reading a mammogram, that the patient has tested positive for the BRCA 1 or 2 gene. Having this information at his or her fingertips can influence how a mammogram is read. Workflow-enabled IT, in fact, is already employed throughout the breast cancer patient process, beginning with the initial diagnosis, prompting for further testing for HER2/neu, and then guiding care pathways based on the specifics of the diagnosis.

Similarly, recent advances in identifying a rare mutation in certain lung cancer tumors enable treatment using a drug that specifically targets the mutation. For some patients in clinical trials conducted at Massachusetts General Hospital with a drug developed by Pfizer, there has been a commute of an almost certain death sentence. One patient, in fact, had undergone chemotherapy with seven different regimens before screening identified that his specific type of advanced non-small cell lung cancer (NSCLC) had the anaplastic lymphoma kinases (ALK) fusion gene.

Today, the five-year survival rate for lung cancer in the United States is only 15 percent, with NSCLC the most prevalent form of lung cancer.[10-11] Researchers now understand that NSCLC cannot be singularly characterized, but instead includes multiple sub-forms of the disease, each with its own molecular signature. Finding molecular targets such as this specific ALK mutation expands understanding and opens the pathway to discovery of other molecular targets and therapies to attack such cancers in every form. Imagine now an IT system that would automatically suggest testing for this mutation or other variations in the disease and then guide the care appropriately.

This is personalized medicine. Does such a tailored approach add to healthcare costs? The answer is no. The benefits in terms of earlier detection and more effective treatments, while eliminating therapies that are ineffective or even harmful, will actually result in costs shifting downward. Simply stated, true personalized medicine will improve both the effectiveness and the efficiency of care.

Managing the Information: Tsunami to Improve Efficiency of Care

All of these advances in medicine are relatively futile if healthcare providers do not have effective means to manage the knowledge and the patient, and that is why HIT systems are no less significant than the clinical discoveries described. HIT is the engine that will drive personalized medicine into mainstream practice. Not only will it bring order to unstructured knowledge, it will also control runaway costs and improve workplace and clinical efficiencies. A core principle of health IT is that information should follow the patient. Perhaps the right approach is that information should not only *follow* the patient, but also *surround* the patient and the care process.

One important way to bring this approach to life is by creating workflows based on best practice protocols. Such workflows can be as simple as managing IVs or as complex as treating a patient with HER2/neu-positive breast cancer. Through HIT-driven best practice workflows, healthcare organizations can ensure compliance with quality standards, cost and time effectiveness of care, and most important, the best clinical outcomes for the patient.

The Potential of *The American Recovery and Reinvestment Act of 2009* (ARRA)

AARA provides $20 billion to support the adoption of HIT by physicians and hospitals. The goal—an impressive one—is to ensure that everyone has an electronic health record (EHR) that follows them throughout their lifetimes. The complexity and size of this undertaking is not to be underestimated, especially when statistics show that only 1.5 percent of U.S. hospitals have an EHR system available across all clinical units.[12]

Whether the incentives and penalties are enough to encourage and ensure adoption and meaningful use of such systems is not yet known. But just consider the potential if HIT is deployed correctly as we have described. The impact on efficiency, the elimination of unnecessary tests, and facilitation of care are really just the most fundamental of benefits.

When EHRs are more widely available, clinicians could then marry a patient's information with analysis of the individual's specific illness against research data of therapies for other individuals with similar manifestations of the same disease. This process is accomplished through clinical IT systems that mine information from bio-statistical databases, clinical evidence, data from across disparate systems, knowledge about protocols, and present it to the clinician in a unified format to support sound and informed decision-making. The result is less trial and error and more effective therapies administered sooner and with greater likelihood of successful outcomes.

Health IT systems are, therefore, not mere repositories but knowledge engines that enable the management of both the individual's history and the ever-increasing body of clinical evidence to support clinicians in determining the most effective treatments available. This is the underlying foundation that brings personalized medicine to the forefront.

No longer will we develop treatments based on patients with similar genetic information, histories, and disease composition. We can use a "pharmacogenomics-centric approach" with drugs and therapies that are designed for smaller subsets of specific patients. Targeting therapies to such specificity—to the characteristics of a disease in smaller communities of patients and even the individual—is much more effective than broad, population-based treatments.

Because the clinician will possess the most current information on the patient and his or her specific disease, the most effective treatment for that individual patient can be administered. To critics who would claim that such a model is one of luxury and not economically sustainable, there is, perhaps, nothing worse or more financially irresponsible than a therapy that is ineffective or that causes harm to a patient.

That is the potential of HIT that the federal government, through a combination of ARRA funding and healthcare reform, hopes to bring to reality. But what of the peril? Is there a downside to HIT adoption? HIT systems improperly designed and improperly used often simply automate existing processes and therefore have little or no impact on quality of care or costs. To be effective, HIT must not just serve as an information repository, but must change clinicians' behavior within the organization and how they use that information. The ARRA will reward providers for meaningful use of IT. Missing from the government's concept is the idea of meaningful systems—ones that are interoperable across healthcare organizations and provider models and that provide both information and knowledge engines.

Pulling All the Levers

At Siemens Healthcare, we hold a unique perspective, having integrated our portfolio to include in-vivo and in-vitro diagnostics, therapies, and workflow-enabled healthcare information technology systems.

Our goal never was to maintain these as separate silos of business and become a technology conglomerate. Instead, we set out from the start to integrate the technologies to transform medicine and healthcare in the 21st century. In fact, it has been the core of our vision to develop the competencies to predict, prevent, diagnose, and treat disease cost-effectively and safely. We believe that by integrating these technologies, we can provide clinicians with the means to both improve the efficiency and efficacy of care, which naturally results in lower costs.

As many industry leaders have noted, the technology to transform care exists today. Molecular diagnosis, physiological imaging, and knowledge-generating IT systems are being used by thousands of clinicians every day. But fundamental change is needed to drive the widespread adoption and use of such ground-breaking technologies.

First, the very practice of medicine must undergo a dramatic change. As referenced earlier, we have a reactive, sick-care system. In the United States, there is no better system to treat complex and catastrophic conditions, but we must take a different approach to chronic diseases and their treatment. To achieve this goal, we must refocus on the medical school classroom, particularly on prediction and prevention as our primary weapons to combat disease. Today, medical school curricula focus on the disease, not the patient, on treating someone who is ill rather than preventing the disease by understanding a patient's biology and genetic composition. If we recall the basic premise of personalized medicine, it is on the individual, not the disease. And, medical schools must embrace HIT as a tool no less vital than the stethoscope. Such a cultural and scientific shift is a complicated undertaking but one with such great promise.

Second, physician payment models must also change. Today's reimbursement is based on a single standard—Medicare and Medicaid payment rates set by government. These rates are arbitrary and do not reflect the true cost of delivering care to the individual. New reimbursement models must take into account customized plans of treatment. For example, one individual's prostate cancer treatment may be very different than his neighbor's. The treatments could be equally effective, but because they are planned for each individual and his or her variation of the disease, the tests used for diagnosis and subsequent treatment plans may be very different. While payers may be faced with a potentially more expensive treatment protocol through this payment model, overall costs may be lowered because patients will receive effective, personalized care. The "guess factor" is eliminated. Additionally, individuals will return to productive lives more quickly, reducing the societal impact.

Third, drug discovery, development, and delivery must be improved. The entire cycle of research and clinical trials must be expedited so that new drugs are discovered and delivered to consumers more quickly. Expediting the regulatory processes at the Food and Drug Administration and developing effective ways to manage clinical trails for small subsets of patients will become the new norm. Real-time post-market surveillance would allow for a streamlined process on the front end since drug efficacy could be more closely monitored on the back end. In an age of blockbuster drugs, this is a difficult issue to tackle.

We are on the cusp of enormous change in healthcare. Between diagnostics, imaging, and knowledge-driven IT, we have the technology to transform care, to prevent many diseases before their onset, to cure them if they occur. This can be our future if we can make the necessary changes to allow it to flourish.

—w—

Thomas J. Miller is the Chief Executive Officer for the Workflow & Solutions Division, Siemens Healthcare. Previously, he was a member of the executive board of Siemens Medical Solutions (now known as Siemens Healthcare). During his initial 15-year tenure with Siemens, Mr. Miller headed up the Magnetic Resonance product division and the U.S. sales and service organization. Subsequently, Mr. Miller was the Vice President, Business Development for Siemens Medical Solutions and Chief Executive Officer of Siemens Medical Solutions Health Services Corporation.

—w—

[1] Dept. of Health and Human Services (HHS), March 30, 2009, http://www.hhs.gov/.

[2] OECD, "Total expenditure on health, per capita US PPP, (Purchasing Power Parity)," http://www.oecd.org/home/0,3305,en_2649_201185_1_1_1_1_1,00.html (accessed January 21, 2010).

[3] Centers for Disease Control and Prevention (CDC), "Chronic Disease Overview," http://www.cdc.gov/chronicdisease/index.htm (accessed on January 15, 2010).

[4] "The Cost of Dying," *60 Minutes*, CBS News, November 22, 2009.

[5] M. Meadows, "Genomics and Personalized Medicine," *FDA Consumer Magazine*, November-December 2006, http://www.fda.gov/fdac/features/2005/605_genomics.html through.

[6] Kathleen Sebelius, Written Testimony of Senate Confirmation Hearing, April 2009.

[7] Balias, et al, "Managing Clinical Knowledge for Healthcare Improvement," *Medical Informatics Yearbook*, 2000.

[8] Family Medicine.

[9] National Cancer Institute, http://www.cancer.gov/.

[10] Pao Horn, "EML4-ALK: Honing In on a New Target in Non–Small-Cell Lung Cancer," *Journal of Clinical Oncology*, Vol. 27, No. 26, September 10, 2009: 4232-4235.

[11] American Cancer Society, www.cancer.gov.

[12] Jha, et al., "Use of Electronic Health Records in U.S. Hospitals," *NEJM*, Volume 360:1628-1638, Number 16, April 16, 2009.

CHAPTER 5

Adaptive Information Technology: Driving Hospital Quality and Efficiency through Process Improvement

Ben Sawyer and Jim Rosenblum

—༄—

Editor's Introduction

W. Edwards Deming once said, "It is not necessary to change. Survival is not mandatory." That perfectly captures the current state of healthcare. For many hospitals and health systems, they understand that models of the 20th century have become the anchors of the 21st century. Few changes are more vital than embracing health information technology. While much of the attention has been on the clinical benefits of health IT, it can also dramatically improve the movement of patients, supplies, staff, and other critical aspects within a hospital. Adaptive technology can be the necessary glue to achieve system-wide peak performance and process improvement, from admission to discharge and all points in between. These kinds of technologies and processes will be essential in the future, particularly given the profound changes that may come from Washington and the demographic shifts on the horizon. Those hospitals and health systems that embrace change and deploy the right technologies to see it through will not only survive but thrive.

—༄—

No one wants to be sick. No one wants to go to the hospital. And as if illness or injury was not enough, Americans often find themselves dealing with long wait times, delays, medical errors, and other preventable irritants. All of this often leads to distrust and distaste for community hospitals.

Results from some patient satisfaction surveys conducted within the past five years suggest a slow but steady decline in public trust and confidence in hospitals. Beyond this loss of trust and confidence, the delays, mistakes, inefficiencies, and miscommunication that patients and their families often experience have far-reaching consequences:

- Healthcare costs and utilization are driven up;
- Quality and patient outcomes are inconsistent;
- Service delivery across the country is highly variable; and,
- Patient, physician, and hospital staff satisfaction is negatively affected.

Problems can be found throughout every process, from admission to treatment to discharge. However, they are merely symptoms of a much larger, systemic problem in our hospitals that is being driven by three interconnected elements:

1. **Lack of coordination.** There is no hospital-wide, inter-departmental coordination within most hospitals. Typically, a hospital is department-centric, acting more like a shopping mall than a single enterprise.

2. **Lack of visibility.** There is no hospital-wide view of throughput, patient flow, and logistics in real time. This leads to speculation and opinion instead of fact-based understanding of how to identify and eliminate process flaws and inefficiencies.

3. **Lack of aim.** There is no hospital-wide initiative, also called system aim, to achieve the needed visibility and inter-departmental coordination to improve patient throughput. Moreover, there is no senior-level executive responsible for its realization.

As Mark Graban pointed out in his 2007 eBook, *How Toyota Can Save Your Life...at the Hospital*, "What we hear in the media are isolated, and sometimes sensationalized, stories of individuals who screw up. What we don't hear about is the systemic nature of these injuries and deaths."[1]

Graban noted that as much as we think these incidences are the result of incompetent caregivers, errors can occur at any time, in any hospital, because our existing systems are failing. One of the root problems lies in how hospitals move patients through their system.

Hospitals essentially operate as a collection of independent departments that compete for the hospital's limited resources, including patient beds, wheelchairs, medications, IV pumps, and other essential diagnostic and treatment resources. The current solution practiced by most hospitals is to attempt to treat systemic problems by repairing the parts. Unfortunately, today's modern hospital is too complex, with too many simultaneous transactions, to effectively sustain process improvements through human effort alone. Yet that is what most hospitals are doing. They are applying state-of-the-art process improvement methodologies but attempting to sustain improved performance through human effort.

This approach is fraught with problems. Let us explore why.

Peak Performance Is Unsustainable without Adaptive Technology

To address the challenges of cost, quality, safety, and utilization, hospitals have turned to other industries to study how they have successfully solved similar operational throughput challenges, including automotive (Toyota), retail (Walmart), and shipping (UPS). While these industries have lowered costs, improved quality, and decreased variability across their entire enterprise, hospitals have not sustained the same success using identical methods.

Why? Because hospitals have not utilized technology to interconnect all their processes or adopted a system-wide aim that makes patient flow the primary focus. When hospitals craft optimized processes that are based on static systems, these processes degrade over time because of the nature of hospitals' dynamic environment. It is within this human intervention that unproductive, wasteful activities occur, causing a bottleneck within the system. The results are delays, inefficiencies, and errors.

Like airport operations, a hospital's goal is to flow all patients simultaneously at their best possible rates with respect to length of stay, service times, quality, safety, and resource consumption.

Admission → Diagnosis → Treatment → Discharge

While the healthcare industry has spent a lot of time developing individual patient care paths for each of these processes, the notion of optimizing *simultaneous* patient throughput gets less attention and is inherently more challenging from an operations standpoint.

Quite frankly, seeing and controlling simultaneous throughput is not possible without an adaptive information technology. Adaptive technology has three primary capabilities:

1. **Flexibility.** It is flexible enough to allow for and adapt to the evolving best practices of process improvement methodology, instead of forcing breakthrough practices to conform to the technology's capabilities.

2. **Capability.** It is capable of steering performance activities toward the organization's overall throughput goal.

3. **Feedback loops.** It provides feedback loops in real time that allow for adjustments to be made within the dynamic environment.

Let us return to the airport analogy to illustrate this concept. Airline reservations and schedules do not translate into smooth logistics on any given day because of constantly changing conditions. Airports manage this chaos with adaptive information technology in the form of a centralized air traffic control center and connected operational control centers which have algorithms that make decisions within these changing conditions.

Most hospitals do not use adaptive technology systems like this. However, these technologies exist and have been proven to sustain the impact of process improvement methodologies within the dynamic environment of hospitals.

Despite this need for adaptive technology in hospitals, it is important to note that technology alone will not sustain performance. Eliminating wasteful activities and confusion throughout the hospital requires a senior-level commitment toward an attainable goal and the appropriate methodology (i.e., performance improvement practices) to optimize the necessary processes.

Peak Performance Begins with a System-Wide Aim

While a simple concept, the power of a system aim to optimize performance cannot be underestimated, particularly given the department-centric operational bias that characterizes today's healthcare systems. In department-centric operations, the lack of a system aim leads to disconnected islands of excellence, which affect system flow in three key ways:

1. **Cross-vertical handoffs do not occur seamlessly.** Ideally, the movement of patients from admission to diagnostics, nursing units, treatment, and finally through discharge occurs without significant delays. In the department-centric hospital, however, one department's needs are not necessarily compatible with another department's priorities. Consequently, there are vacant beds that could be occupied by revenue-generating patients who are kept waiting somewhere else.

2. **Inputs and outputs are controlled at a departmental— not system—level.** Unless the hospital is on diversion, the usual patient entry points (i.e., admissions and the emergency department) have little or no control over their inputs. In other words, they are expected to accommodate all patients who show up. Problems arise when other departments, such as nursing units, limit their inputs, causing a backlog of patients and making it difficult to deliver patient care according to prescribed protocols.

3. **Efficiencies gained in one department do not necessarily contribute to system-wide patient flow.** Frequently, when departmental flow is optimized at the department level (i.e., sub-optimized) as opposed to across the system as a whole, poor system throughput performance is the result. For example, if the emergency department boosts its efficiency, but did not coordinate with a similar endeavor

in the nursing units, particularly the critical care units, the number of emergency department boarder patients will increase. Boarder patients are those patients whose emergency care has been completed and for whom the ED physician disposition has recommended an inpatient admission, and yet they remain waiting in the ED for inpatient beds one hour or more after the dispositions have been completed. This sub-optimization process often occurs to the detriment of the organization's overall throughput.

Eliminating Activities That Waste Time and Resources

The greatest potential for improving hospital performance across every process is in identifying and eliminating wasteful, non-value added activities and use of resources, also known as white space. Waste or white space includes activities such as resource overuse, unnecessary transportation, unused inventory, staffing miscommunication, duplication of services, and patient waiting.

In a hospital, these white space opportunities typically are found where important handoffs and coordination take place. They occur when nurses are coordinating diagnostics, procedures, and services for patients, but patients are not receiving direct attention and care. For example, in a unit transfer, a case manager or nurse will call bed management to request a bed. Once a bed is identified, the patient has to be transported to the room. Waste occurs with unnecessary phone calls, voice messages, and staff activity that have nothing to do with caring for the patient or moving the patient through the system. Bed management may wait hours before an appropriate bed is available. If the unit transfer involves a complex patient, it may take multiple phone calls and coordination to secure the right resources to actually move the patient from one unit to another. These are only a few simple examples of the layers of logistical contraints and bottlenecks that choke hospital throughput efficiency, causing waits and delays, and which jeopardize patient safety, satisfaction, and organizational performance.

Adaptive technology provides the organization-wide view of where every patient is, their current status, and what remains to be done. For example, patient and order logistics can provide patient itineraries to nurses for more effective management of the day's work demands, and real-time rounding lists for physicians who need immediate order and patient location status to make their rounds as efficient as possible. Adaptive technology also allows hospital managers to identify areas of white space and to then implement processes to eliminate that white space. In the case of a transport order in the example above, an adaptive system can assign and notify the nearest transporter responsible for the task, so that they do not have to travel all the way back to their base station before accepting the next transportation task.

The diagrams below explain the process of identifying white space, then reducing or eliminating it.

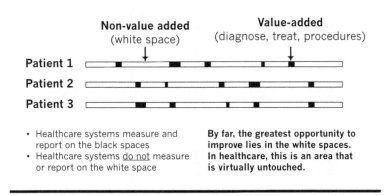

- Healthcare systems measure and report on the black spaces
- Healthcare systems do not measure or report on the white space

By far, the greatest opportunity to improve lies in the white spaces. In healthcare, this is an area that is virtually untouched.

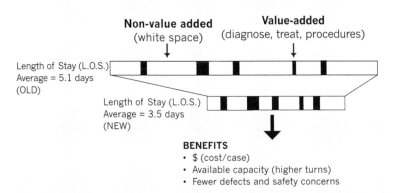

"THE AVERAGE PATIENT CASE"

BENEFITS
- $ (cost/case)
- Available capacity (higher turns)
- Fewer defects and safety concerns

Case Study: Mercy St. Vincent Medical Center

Mercy St. Vincent Medical Center, a 400+ bed teaching hospital in northern Ohio, is the critical care regional referral center within the Mercy Health Partners (MHP) system.[2] Its story illustrates how an acclaimed hospital, at the forefront of performance improvement practices, implemented an adaptive system and achieved significant improvements. It demonstrates that methodology alone will not achieve sustainable process improvements. The team at Mercy has embraced all aspects of process improvement: centralized leadership control, system aim, and adaptive technology.

By all external standards, Mercy St. Vincent has been a high-performing hospital for many years, winning a top 100 hospital designation, earning a JD Powers & Associates top performer award, and rating equally well on other standards of performance like patient satisfaction scores, regulatory compliance, and core measure outcomes.

Like many distinguished hospitals, Mercy St. Vincent has already initiated a LEAN and Six Sigma department in 2006, a DRG assurance program, employee retention and training programs, a top-ranked patient satisfaction improvement program, and an electronic medical record system with computerized physician order entry. However, patient throughput problems persisted, which negatively affected organizational performance measures.

The recent downturn in the economy hit the northern Ohio market particularly hard, causing the unemployment rate to climb to 15 percent and exacerbating the challenges Mercy St. Vincent already faced. As expected, non-pay cases increased and elective procedures diminished.

A System-Wide Audit

Mercy St. Vincent began with a system-wide operational audit to map its current processes, including wasteful activities. This operational audit revealed that the hospital was not functioning as an integrated system. As is typical with hospitals, it was an assemblage of disconnected islands of excellence. This explained why many of the previous performance efforts, which had been layered one on top of another, had not yet resulted in breakthrough system-wide performance.

Key findings of the audit found the following:

- System-wide patient flow lacked leadership and a senior executive who owned it;
- There were no clear system-level throughput or capacity-related key performance indicators;
- Department-level performance improvement efforts were under way; however, those efforts did not create improved system throughput performance;
- Competition existed between departments for internal resources such as beds, wheelchairs, and intravenous units; and,
- Responses to patient and resource flow challenges were reactionary. For example, admission requests during high census often resulted in multiple phone calls and visits to nursing units to check on bed availability rather than instant responses to admission demand based upon a clear and visible understanding of hospital-wide capacity.

Once the root challenges were understood and prioritized, Mercy St. Vincent's senior team defined a clear system aim for their patient throughput efforts, which they refer to as "Patient first, journey to zero." This means zero errors, zero defects, and zero rework. This new perspective has helped Mercy St. Vincent make important changes that would otherwise not have been initiated.

Once Mercy St. Vincent executives defined their system aim, it became the lens through which they evaluated every current-state flow process, role, and function. Patient flows from admission through discharge were simultaneously evaluated.

Leadership then complemented the audit and evaluation by implementing a new adaptive technology. This technology was a hospital operating system developed by StatCom, an Atlanta-based software company, which allows management and staff to design new process patterns and outline performance goals.[3]

The existing process for getting a patient into a bed from the time of the incoming call required was taking more than three hours, on average. When the process was completed the average time dropped below 50 minutes. The technology gave everyone operational data and analytics that helped drive informed decision-making, including:

1. Access to raw data for manipulation within tools such as Excel and Crystal Reports. Information that can be gleaned includes detailed throughput metrics by department.

2. Standardized reports, such as discharge turnaround time by hour and estimated length of stay achievement by unit.

3. Real-time operational dashboards for executives, bed management, nursing, case management, transportation, and housekeeping represent operational dashboards that are made available to all of the various operational areas requiring real-time information in support of system flow.

This technology supported Mercy St. Vincent's establishment of a centralized care coordination hub that effectively manages system-wide patient throughput operations. New flow processes were translated into standard operating procedures, with a comprehensive training program designed for front-line staff. Case management was moved into the forefront of operations and patient-flow logistics, and care coordinators were designated in each operational unit to be closely aligned with the hub. In essence, Mercy St. Vincent adopted a similar hub-and-spoke model used at airports.

Within the first year of initiating this integrated approach, and in spite of a depressed economic market, Mercy St. Vincent was able to:

- Reduce patients' average length of stay by 14.3 percent;
- Lower direct costs by $8.6 million;
- Increase admission volume by 11.2 percent;
- Improve quality and safety performance outcomes; and,
- Achieve total financial impact in one year of $10.3 million.

According to the Georgia Institute of Technology's Health Systems Institute, which provided a third-party validation of these first-year results, Mercy St. Vincent will continue to achieve year-to-year improvements of $13 to $17 million as operations are transformed.

In order to sustain its improvements, Mercy St. Vincent's future state processes were hardwired into the existing system to adapt to the dynamic interconnectedness of the daily chaos. Operational analytics from the adaptive system were aligned with critical path milestones and designed to keep Mercy St. Vincent up-to-date on progress and to alert executives when adjustments were necessary. Mercy St. Vincent realized its patient throughput potential and achieved remarkable results in one year.

As the awards and recognition achieved by Mercy St. Vincent prior to beginning its operational transformation demonstrate, many hospitals achieve recognition for comparative performance and yet still have not reached their full operational potential. As long as hospitals are constrained by the gravitational pull of department-centric operations, benchmarking is flawed and real throughput breakthroughs will remain elusive.

Transforming How Hospitals Achieve Peak Performance

It's time for process initiatives in healthcare to achieve the same level of respect and impact they have in other industries. However, like in other industries, these initiatives must be adapted and customized to the unique and ever-changing environment of the hospitals that can benefit from them.

Hospitals are too complicated for human effort alone to sustain improvements. If they continue their current efforts to optimize patient throughput without the foundation of an adaptive technology, they will encounter the same frustrations. Staff will burn out and change roles. Improvement gains will continue to degrade over time. Preventable errors will steadily occur. Patients will stay in hospitals too long, driving up the cost of their care.

Can you imagine an airport that operated solely on radio communications and human-calculated algorithms? Can you imagine

NASA launching a rocket relying solely on human intuition and effort? It is time for hospital operations to be built on the back of adaptive technology instead of human performance alone. As other industry transformations have demonstrated, adaptive technology can become the engine driving sustainable performance over time.

—⚊—

Ben Sawyer is the Executive Vice President of StatCom, an operating entity of Jackson Healthcare. With more than 25 years of experience in managing healthcare operations, he is responsible for the sales, product management, and client service operations for StatCom. Mr. Sawyer has taken a lead role in developing the industry's first hospital operating system. He was the executive responsible for system-wide performance and process improvement, and served as the quality council chair for St. Mary's Health Care System. Mr. Sawyer also managed multiple operational service lines within two other health systems.

Jim Rosenblum is the Executive Vice President, Products and Chief Technology Officer for StatCom. He is focused on defining StatCom's product strategy and development, which includes leading the development of the industry's first hospital operating system. Most recently, he served as Chief Technology Officer for Emmi Solutions, where he was integral in shaping the technology vision, strategic planning, developing software, and managing product development and information technology departments.

—⚊—

[1] Mark Graban, *How Toyota Can Save Your Life...at the hospital* (2007), http://changethis.com/32.02.HowToyotaCanSave.

[2] Catholic Healthcare Partners, http://www.mercyweb.org (accessed January 21, 2010).

[3] StatCom, http://www.statcom.com (accessed January 21, 2010).

CHAPTER 6

Picturing a Cure:
A Patient-Centered Approach to Cancer Care

Chad A. Eckes

—ɷ—

Editor's Introduction

Cancer. The word alone is chilling. If you are one of the 1.5 million Americans diagnosed with cancer every year, the fear, stress, and confusion can be overwhelming. Thankfully, over the past several years, we have begun to turn the tide in the war on cancer. Breakthrough treatments, earlier detection, and innovative therapies are showing dramatic progress. While these advances are vital to a patient fighting the disease, so too is a dedicated team of skilled, passionate professionals. And when that team combines the latest medical innovations with health information technology, the hopes of beating, preventing, and then eliminating cancer can be realized. That is what the Cancer Treatment Centers of America (CTCA) has done. By deploying a comprehensive electronic medical record system across all its facilities, CTCA is providing better, safer care with higher customer satisfaction rates than ever before. Just as new breakthroughs become widely adopted to combat cancer, CTCA has shown that health IT should be as well.

—ɷ—

Maria Milam had a unique way of explaining to her four-year-old son Andrew what advanced kidney cancer was doing to her body. "I showed him his blood vessels," says Maria. "You have little soldiers in there to fight germies. Mommy has to take medicine to help the soldiers fight the germies."

Maria's doctors at CTCA, however, have a little more advanced way of explaining what is going on inside her body and how treatment is affecting her disease, thanks to our electronic health record (EHR) system. The 41-year-old Wake Forest, North Carolina, woman is one of thousands of patients who travel an average of 500 miles every year for our integrative model of care. They all benefit from the safety, security, and efficiency of the EHR system.

"When I sit down with my radiation oncologist, he can just pull up my scans right there in front of me on his laptop computer," says Maria.

Maria's treatment, like the treatment all patients receive at CTCA's network of destination cancer hospitals across the country, includes a comprehensive array of traditional and complementary therapies to fight her cancer and improve her quality of life, designed and delivered by a diverse group of medical experts. These include medical oncologists, surgical oncologists, radiation oncologists, nutritionists, naturopathic doctors, cancer rehabilitation therapists, mind-body specialists, spiritual advisors, and other professionals, all working together to fight Maria's tumors and to support her body, mind, and spirit.

In a given day, Maria may meet with eight or nine of these experts, and it is essential that each of them has timely data on the care that is being refined and delivered to her. One can only imagine what the timeliness of the information flow was like under a paper-record system. Thanks to our EHR system, Maria's records are up-to-the-minute as she talks to each of her care team members.

Dr. Anthony Perre, Chief of Medicine and Lead Hospitalist at CTCA in Philadelphia, says that the EHR system has made explaining complex medical terms and problems quite simple. "Today I saw a gentleman who had a bowel obstruction who said, 'I'd like to see what that looks like,'" says Dr. Perre. "So I pulled out my laptop and showed it to him. A picture is worth a thousand words. Now I can bring in my laptop and show my patients what they are dealing with."

In Record Speed

On October 1, 2006, implementation of the EHR system began; on March 28, 2008, it went live. In December 2008, CTCA opened its newest treatment center in suburban Phoenix as the nation's first all-digital cancer hospital, with its other three hospitals quickly approaching fully digital status. This new system allows us to bring patients more personalized, patient-centered care. The EHR system is an electronic data management system that makes it possible for all our physicians and clinicians to work collaboratively from one automated and comprehensive patient record. With real-time access to centralized information, the EHR system enables patients' entire care team to communicate more effectively with each other about the progress of their treatment.

CTCA made the decision that instead of a phased-in approach, it would shut down 18 legacy systems and activate 22 integrated modules of a major EHR system. The project was further challenged by integrating large cultural changes, including standardization of clinical processes/orders/formulary, adoption of computerized physician order entry (CPOE), and movement from paper-based to electronic documentation. To accomplish all this, leadership mapped out all future work processes down to the daily work task level and then designed the system around the processes. The blueprint begins when the patient first calls and extends through oncology after-care. It is a philosophy that many organizations talk about but rarely achieve in practice. The result of this approach was a complete change in how employees did their jobs.

Prior to EHR implementation, the aging system was no longer meeting users' needs. In a normal healthcare system, if an MRI or an X-ray is ordered, hours or days can elapse before the patient arrives to complete the order, which typically does not pose a problem. At CTCA, such a situation was an issue because patients were often traveling long distances to get treatment. Patients were actually moving faster than their paper medical records through the clinical processes. This was the first catalyst for the EHR system— to allow records to move faster.

"To be able to go to any part of the building and have the records there is huge," says Maria. "No one is running around looking for your records like they would be if I were in a regular healthcare system. It makes the experience more efficient and gives me more confidence."

All research shows that getting the information to the patients via EHRs provides better, safer care and yields better customer satisfaction. With respect to customer satisfaction, there is something powerful about providing a visual image of an MRI and pointing to it, which helps a patient understand. In the past, doctors could show patients their X-rays by bringing them to an X-ray box or PACS viewing station, but even this would be an image of very low quality. Today, our personnel can show patients their images in the context of their medical histories to provide a complete view of their records.

The Mother Standard

An important catalyst for the EHR system can be traced back to the founding principles of CTCA. Richard J. Stephenson founded CTCA nearly 30 years ago in memory of his mother, Mary Brown Stephenson, who died of cancer following what he and his family felt was the extremely disappointing care she received. But it is Stephenson's mother and all mothers and fathers battling health problems who have inspired our hospitals to make healthcare more accessible, reliable, and immediate through information technology. It is what we call the "Mother Standard" of care. Every patient is treated with the same warmth, unconditional support, and respect one would give to a parent or loved one.

Safety First

The most critical catalyst for the EHR system is patient safety. Every time someone handles a paper record, there is an opportunity for error. If the physician puts the information directly into the system electronically, it reduces the opportunity for error dramatically.

"At CTCA, we want to practice what we preach," says Dr. Perre. "It's a patient-centered approach at CTCA, and we want patient safety to be of the utmost importance. EHR and specifically CPOE are proven to improve patient safety."

Nurses are trained to double-check all medications. But because of busy schedules and an inefficient, paper-based system, there is always room for human error. An EHR, on the other hand, utilizes bar-coding, which helps better ensure that the correct dose goes to the right patient.

The system also has built-in technology to prevent physician error. If a physician orders a drug at the wrong dose for the patient's body weight, the system flags it. In order to bypass this warning, the physician must make a notation as to why the higher dosage is necessary, which helps guard against accidents. For example, if a physician meant to put in 10 mg of a certain medication, but puts in 100 instead, the system catches the mistake. Similar logic is built around allergies, medication interactions, and recommendations for orders based upon evidence.

"As a physician, I must say that our handwriting does stink," says Dr. Perre. "I can't tell you how frustrating it is when you have to go back and call another physician to ask what he or she has written about a patient. When you do that with every patient, that can become tedious and the potential for misinterpretation is huge. We know that medical errors are a possibility and we have come to realize how important it is to minimize these errors."

Experiencing Efficiency

Beyond minimizing errors, EHRs make healthcare and the patient's experience much more efficient.

Maria had not been feeling well for many years before she was diagnosed at age 40. She went to her general practitioner, who told her that at 215 pounds, she needed to lose some weight if she wanted to have more energy. The physician also suggested that raising a four-year-old and a two-year-old at her age was draining her energy levels. "At one point, I turned to the nurse and said, 'I am too young to feel this old and this exhausted all of the time,'" says Maria.

So after switching to a new doctor and finally being diagnosed with advanced-stage kidney cancer, instead of emotionally falling apart, Maria had a very different reaction.

"At first I felt huge relief because I knew something was wrong with me and I didn't feel like anyone believed me," she says.

Like most patients at CTCA, Maria had already been treated at another hospital. In the end, her choice was our hospital located in Philadelphia. As her cancer continued to spread, even after eight months of treatment at the previous facility, Maria sought an alternative place for care, knowing that efficiency was important to her treatment. "With my illness, since it is so advanced, time is of the essence," she notes. "It makes me comfortable knowing that everyone is up-to-date because things can change one day to the next."

"I Can't Imagine Going Back to Paper"

Getting all the physicians and clinicians prepared for the new EHR system took some work. It took tremendous amounts of training—at times more than 80 hours per physician—before going live. While the aim was 40 hours of training for physicians and between 60 and 80 hours for nurses, in reality it was based on individual levels of understanding. We utilized multidisciplinary education by using different approaches to training, including computer-based, classroom, and one-on-one mentoring. Though approximately 80 "super users"— those with greater expertise in dealing with the EHR system—were integrated per hospital, the level of change should not be underestimated. Most physicians and clinicians have not been trained to integrate computers like this into their care practices.

With a change of this magnitude, there will always be a productivity impact at first. Before the go-live date, some natural anxiousness set in. Periods of frustration resulted as people experienced change in their work environments and workloads. The key to addressing the tension was open and frequent communication, an agile process to make changes, and "super users'" availability for training and consultation. As predicted, the change process took approximately six months for full utilization and acceptance by staff.

"There was trepidation, but also excitement about patient safety," says Dr. Perre. "Most of the trepidation centered upon the documentation process. How much time, how effective, and how easy would it be?

"We are all trying to see so many patients in a timely manner, so if it takes longer to document patient visits because of entering them into the EHR, that is a concern. It was a major adjustment," notes Dr. Perre. Prior to the EHR system, physicians and clinicians would treat the patient and document the visit after the fact. In the EHR world, the documentation is integrated into the patient care process, which in the end, maximizes caregiver time.

"They gave us the education we needed to make the transition easy," says Dr. Perre. "They trained what they called 'super users' on the floor to help. A super user is someone who has gone through the process of learning what the system can and cannot do and has dedicated a lot of time."

Dr. Perre said that within a few weeks he was as productive with the EHR system as he was prior to its implementation.

"I didn't have to hunt for charts. All the information was there and available for me, which offset any time delays," he says. "Even the documentation process is easier. There are ways to quicken it up—ways to use abbreviations that we make ourselves, so there is flexibility in the system.

"In the beginning, while there was an adjustment period, it was a very short period. I can't imagine going back to paper. It really has become easier," he notes.

Putting the Patient in Charge

Putting patients in charge of their data and use, or "patient empowerment," is a guiding philosophy of ours. That is why soon, not only will physicians and clinicians have access to the EHR system, but patients will too. A patient portal is scheduled to be completed by July 2010, enabling all patients to have direct access to their data.

The patient portal will be available on an Internet site, where the patient will log in with his or her username and password to securely access the health record. Patients will have the ability to export the data to Microsoft HealthVault, instead of having to ask staff for their records or to burn a copy of a CD.

It also provides up-to-the-minute data, and the system can alert patients in real time with a text, e-mail, or call when lab or other test results are ready. While a physician is not present to explain the results, most patients are well educated in terms of their care and results. The key is to enable patients to receive immediate answers if they have questions, including the ability to have a secure, online dialogue with their clinicians and physicians.

Placing a Premium on Paperless

Going paperless allows organizations to reduce the costs of paper, storage, data entry employees, transcriptionists, etc. More important, one must consider the efficiency a company can gain from utilizing an EHR system. Other efficiencies to note include:

- **Increasing revenues:** Revenues increased because physicians and clinicians now see more patients in the same amount of time. Moreover, face time with each individual patient is not sacrificed.
- **Removing administrative waste:** Removing waste on the back end enables additional revenue growth while also reducing expenses.
- **Improving coding accuracy:** Improving accuracy in many cases revealed that physicians were charging too little.
- **Combining for the sake of ease:** Previously, CTCA had eighteen legacy systems with different hardware maintenance and support costs and now has only one.

This is all predicated on having access to the data. Most people think the risk of data access is easily managed because if the system goes down, staff can go back to paper. However, we no longer use paper-based processes and have retrained all staff accordingly. Five layers of data backup have been built, along with two levels of backup power and a data center that is synchronized in real time. The system is ready for even the most extreme natural disaster.

The World as CTCA Sees IT

Our vision is to empower patients by providing them with the necessary data to make informed decisions. Providing patients with data helps in three different ways: (1) clinical outcomes analysis and management, (2) clinical decision support, and (3) sharing of data across providers in an interoperable fashion.

We have begun our clinical outcomes initiatives. The goal of this initiative is also threefold: (1) demonstrating via data that treatment plans are superior, (2) using minable data to reach more patients needing help, and most importantly, (3) improving upon clinical protocols and guidelines using evidence gained from previous experiences. This initiative hopes to create a scenario of a patient sitting down with his or her oncologist, who inputs demographic, lifestyle, genetic, and specific disease information into the system, which in turn triangulates that information against all the previous patients treated. The output of such clinical guidelines will quantitatively show physicians which treatments are more effective based upon previous evidence. This system would also conduct real-time "what if" analyses to see the potential effectiveness of adding, removing, or modifying certain orders in the guideline. Because patients are empowered to make the clinical decisions at CTCA, it is critical that they be provided with this level of decision facilitation based upon evidence—the clinical guidelines data mining makes this happen.

The same data that can be used to facilitate patient decision-making is also capable of providing evidence-based suggestions to the physician in the form of alerts, recommended guidelines, and cross-checks. Some of this functionality is available today; however, this system has an opportunity to expand the clinical decision support to a whole new level by going beyond flagging potential wrong behaviors and suggesting more effective practices.

The current healthcare IT environment provides a tremendous opportunity to remove administrative waste and improve patient care by enabling sharing of healthcare information across healthcare organizations. Our EHR system has been designed to easily import and export information following clinical care record standards. We are eager to put that openness to good use by connecting to regional and national healthcare information exchanges.

Focus on the Future

The stimulus money provided in the *American Recovery and Reinvestment Act of 2009* will eventually lead all hospital systems to switch to EHRs. If they do not adhere to the mandate, there will be penalties. But our example shows that, more important than complying to regulations, hospitals everywhere should comply because it is the right thing to do for patients. Better patient care is precisely the reason CTCA began an aggressive implementation of its EHR system in 2006.

National Coordinator for Health Information Technology David Blumenthal stresses that health IT must help make the healthcare system work better for patients and providers. Meaningful use metrics should be about the goals of care—quality, speed, and cost—not the technology. We share the view of health IT as a powerful tool to improve the lives of patients and will deliver a clinical culture that maximizes the value of patient care and safety through EHRs.

Among the key objectives suggested in the Office of the National Coordinator's "meaningful use" plan are: adoption of EHRs and CPOE, providing the patient transparent access to that information; efficient and effective sharing of that information across healthcare institutions; and, adherence to quality standards that are evidence-based at providing higher-quality outcomes. Beyond the EHR, the objectives to be accomplished are currently in motion or positioned on a road map for completion within the next 12 months at CTCA.

As for patient Maria Milam, the EHR system her providers used to treat her cancer reduced her stress by eliminating administrative and logistical burdens. Now she is able to concentrate on the things that matter most to her.

"When I arrived at CTCA the first time, I had already filled out the forms at home, so I went straight to the oncology clinic and I have never had to fill out another form again," she says. "I just showed up, they put my wrist band on, and I waited for my appointment. That is unheard of elsewhere.

"None of us know how long we will be here, so I want the best quality of life I can have," she notes. "I still have to manage my illness, but now that is all I have to manage. I can hang out with my kids and get on with my life. My future's so bright, I've gotta wear shades."

—⅏—

Chad A. Eckes is the Chief Information Officer of CTCA, a national network of destination cancer hospitals. CTCA provides a fully integrative care model that combines the best traditional medical care to treat the cancer with scientifically supported complementary therapies to help manage side effects, strengthen the immune system, and improve each patient's quality of life. At CTCA, Mr. Eckes leads a dynamic information technology department in providing innovative technology solutions that improve patient care.

CHAPTER 7

Modernizing the Business Side of Healthcare with Electronic Administration

Julie D. Klapstein*

—ɯ—

Editor's Introduction

The focus of health IT has long been on improving the delivery of care, but it can also improve its administration. While every other major sector of the economy has embraced electronic administration, more than half of the healthcare industry's 18 billion yearly financial transactions are still paper-based.[1] Ninety percent of all medical claims are paid by printing a paper check and mailing it through the U.S. Postal Service. Electronic payment, like PayPal for health, could alone save an estimated $11 billion every year.[2] The tools and technology exist today to modernize the business side of healthcare, and there are pioneers from all sides of the industry—vendors, health plans, and providers—who have shown its benefits. The challenge once again is to convince various stakeholders to embrace change, align incentives to expedite its progress, and migrate its adoption nationwide.

—ɯ—

Throughout my career in health information technology (HIT), I have witnessed and taken part in the technical advancements that have positively impacted the delivery of healthcare to consumers. All of us have experienced the innovation of the Internet in transforming our lives by opening our access to information beyond what we could have imagined just a few decades ago.

I have seen hospitals transform and improve the way they manage internal records by implementing system-wide information systems. With the Internet as an enabler, leading-edge hospitals

* I would like to thank my colleagues at Availity, Russ Thomas, President and Chief Operating Officer, and Kathleen Hertzog, Vice President of Marketing and Communications, for their contributions to this chapter and their valuable leadership in the industry.

are no longer silos within the healthcare industry but are connected to a broader stakeholder community. As a result, we have improved the communication of critical healthcare information and outcomes and have driven cost out of the system. Each time a new technology was adopted by a global corporation or had touched an individual, the world was a better place.

In 2001, I joined Availity, then a start-up health information network in Florida, as its CEO and first employee. The company was founded on the collaboration of two major health plans—fierce competitors—to develop and deliver a multi-health plan web portal for physicians. The intent was to provide a service that would enable physicians and other Florida healthcare providers to more easily and effectively interact with the health plan community. The goal was "administrative simplification"—to reduce unnecessary time and money spent on insurance-related paperwork, phone calls, and faxes, freeing up physicians to spend more time on patient care. Our tagline, "Patients, not paperwork," reflected our mission to improve healthcare delivery by driving inefficiency from the system.

I knew similar projects had failed, but I believed that Availity had the formula for success: collaboration among a limited number of key regional health plans, a limited geographic focus, and a clearly defined scope of initial capabilities. I spent significant time with our company co-founders addressing the reasons our predecessors had failed and understanding the kinds of technologies that physicians and health plans would adopt and utilize.

Through our research, we identified four fundamental tenets:

1. Physicians and other providers want **one place** where they can access the majority of health plan information they require to operate their businesses;
2. Information must be presented in a **common, consistent format**;
3. Information must be **current and accurate** to be of value to the user; and,
4. Access to information must be **quick and easy** in order to be useful.

All of this seems like common sense, but these tenets present real barriers to the broad adoption of available technologies by providers. Moreover, they have prevented the industry from realizing the transformative benefits information technology can provide. They are not, however, impossible to overcome. By focusing on the fundamentals and building a solid foundation with our provider base, we were able to succeed where others had failed. Here is how each of these tenets helped contribute to our goal of improving healthcare delivery through collaboration.

One Place

Give us one place that gives us access to most of our health plans and we will use it. Ask us to learn multiple sites and it just won't happen—we simply don't have that kind of time.

> Cortnie Fricot
> Practice Management Coordinator
> GMS Florida West Coast, Inc.
> Tampa, Florida

Imagine yourself managing a physician practice. Your physicians provide care for thousands of patients, perhaps tens of thousands. You are ultimately responsible for acquiring the most current insurance information on all of them, including eligibility and benefits, plan benefit design, billing, and payment. You have to call each separate health plan to get this information and answer the following questions: Is the patient actually eligible for benefits? What are they eligible for? Do they have a co-pay? Have they satisfied their deductible? What is the status of the claim submitted three weeks ago? Has payment been sent yet?

If you are lucky, each individual health plan may have a website you can access online to find this information. But that means you have to access multiple sites with different usernames and passwords, and learn how each site operates. What you end up with is a lot of time wasted making phone calls, waiting for answers, and learning and re-learning new systems. This process can take so much time that at least one full-time employee is needed to manage it all.

Common, Consistent Format

Knowing where to find the information we need—no matter which health plan it is—saves us so much time and effort.

> Judi Lento, BSH, CMPE
> Practice Administrator
> Sekine, Rasner & Brock, MD, PA
> Jacksonville, Florida

Simply providing access to information is not enough for providers to adopt and use the service at the level required to have a meaningful impact. The information must be presented in a consistent, logical format regardless of the source. This means that even when a user is able to access a single resource for eligibility and benefits information, if each health plan's information is presented in a different format, the practice is still unreasonably burdened with learning how to interpret and navigate multiple presentations of similar information. Time and resources continue to be wasted on administrative tasks and result in depressed utilization rates, translating into lost opportunity for quality and cost improvement.

Current and Accurate

It does us no good to work from old information. We have to have the most current patient information from the health plan to ensure that we are spending our time on the right things.

> Merrilee Severino, CPC, CMM, CPM
> Revenue Management Consultant
> Tampa, Florida

Most of us are accustomed to making decisions in our daily lives using real-time information. And yet in healthcare, physicians too often work with latency in their workflow. This lack of access to real-time information creates administrative headaches for the providers, forcing them to make decisions based on the information at hand. If that information is outdated and inaccurate, the likelihood that they will have to go back and rework a decision is high. Moreover, real-time information access is only going to become more important as increasing numbers of individuals enroll in high-deductible health plans. These plans shift responsibility for a good portion of the provider payments from the health plans to the patients. With consumer bad debt for providers at $60 billion annually, providers must be afforded real-time access to information that tells them what the patient owes.[3] This level of bad debt coupled with an increasing reliance on the patient for payment could spell financial disaster for many care providers.

Quick and Easy

It doesn't just have to be fast, it has to be easy for us to want to use it. If it's complicated, we just don't have the time to devote to learning it—we have too many other things going on.

> Cortnie Fricot
> Practice Management Coordinator
> GMS Florida West Coast, Inc.

We have learned that you can provide the most accurate information from multiple sources in one place, but if users cannot get to the information quickly and easily, they will not use it. Keep it simple, but make sure it is fast. One or two bad experiences are often all it takes to lose a user, and the cost to get that user reengaged and retrained is an unnecessary cost in the system.

So What Is the Solution?

Technology exists today that can solve these problems. The Health Insurance Portability and Accountability Act (HIPAA) defined standards for the exchange of administrative information that have been widely adopted. Most physician offices have adopted some kind of technology, such as practice management systems, to help streamline administrative tasks in their practices. In fact, 89 percent of physicians nationwide say the Internet is "essential to professional practice."[4] Hospitals are some of the most wired organizations in healthcare, with nearly 80 percent using some type of internal technology system.[5] But these systems have not yet solved the problem yet.

Collaboration among all stakeholders is the key to making technology work so that all administrative barriers are broken down. Providers, hospitals, health plans, software vendors, and networks all must be active participants for the industry to realize the time- and cost-saving benefits technology can provide.

What traditionally have been viewed as competitive differentiators must be put aside if we are to succeed in simplifying how healthcare is delivered and administered. The industry requires a shift from a "my web portal is better than your web portal" mentality to a "we make the industry better when we collaborate" position.

Is it a tall order? Is it even possible? The answers are "yes" and "yes."

The Florida Market: A Case Study for the Nation

Florida is an excellent model for collaborative health information exchange. Providers, hospitals, labs, commercial health plans, software vendors, clearinghouses, and, most recently, state governments have all come together as active participants in a single network for sharing health information. The collaboration has resulted in statewide adoption and utilization of real-time electronic administrative transactions. All Florida hospitals, 94 percent of physician offices, and 85 percent of health plans exchange health information using the Availity web portal. More than 120 million healthcare interactions occur annually over this network.

Physician practices, hospitals, and other providers of care simply register online for portal access. Once registered, they receive unique user identification names and passwords that enable real-time communication with multiple health plans on a variety of topics. For example, the most common inquiry from providers to health plans is patient eligibility and benefits. The portal user selects "eligibility and benefits" from a menu of options and completes the required fields, which are the same for all health plans. Responses are returned in seconds, formatted and displayed the same way for all plans.

Healthcare providers may also send claims; inquire on the status of claims already submitted; request treatment authorizations;

submit patient referrals to specialists; send electronic prescriptions; estimate patient expenses; collect patient payment; and review patient health record information, including diagnosis and treatment history, prescriptions, lab orders, and lab results where available.

The savings to physicians and hospitals in moving from paper to electronic interactions are significant:

Transaction	Savings per Electronic Transaction[6]
Eligibility and Benefits	$2.95
Claim Submission	$3.73
Claim Status	$3.33
Claim Remittance	$1.49

Even conservatively, the provider savings are in the hundreds of millions of dollars for a single state. Additionally, studies have shown that health plans save millions of dollars every year by converting from telephone verification of benefits to electronic verification.[7] If these same results could be achieved nationwide, we could make a real dent in the trillions of dollars spent every year on healthcare.

Success, however, did not come easily, nor did it come overnight. It required stakeholders to adopt new ways of interacting and thinking about health information access and exchange. It required true collaboration among competitors and customers alike. It meant accepting a level playing field for the betterment of healthcare delivery in Florida.

Specialty Physician Office: Sekine, Rasner & Brock, MD, PA

The obstetrics and gynecology practice of Sekine, Rasner & Brock has been providing comprehensive healthcare to the women of Jacksonville, Florida, for more than 25 years. The practice includes four board-certified OB/GYNs, three certified nurse midwives, and a small customer service staff.

Judi Lento, B.S.H., C.M.P.E., has been the practice administrator since 1999. When she learned in 2001 about a multi-payer web portal that provided electronic access to multiple health plans offered at no cost to healthcare providers in Florida, she quickly signed on. Judi and her team began to realize the benefits right away. Less time was being spent on the phone verifying patient eligibility, benefits information, and the status of claims filed with health plans. For this specialty practice, managing the referral and treatment authorization process became immensely easier and far less time-consuming

"Conservatively, I would say we won back more than 25 to 30 hours of productivity per week," Lento explained. "From a financial perspective, we estimate our savings at $50,000 to $100,000 per year by having access to this information online. The difference between our pace and efficiency before this service was available is like comparing a snail to a Ferrari."

As additional health plans joined the network, the practice has continued to drive down its administrative costs and avoided the need to add more administrative staff.

Primary Care Practice: GMS Florida West Coast, Inc.

GMS Florida West Coast, Inc. was formed in 1997 by a group of local primary care physicians in Hillsborough and Pinellas counties. The group has grown to 16 sites and a total of 43 providers throughout Hillsborough, Pinellas, and Pasco counties.

Cortnie Fricot, practice management coordinator at GMS, credits electronic access to patient eligibility, benefits, and financial information for driving down costs and improving efficiency at GMS. She estimates the practice would spend at least $500,000 more every year on staff and overhead without the portal. "We were early adopters of electronic health information exchange and started out by managing our referrals online about 10 years ago. As a primary care organization, this was a very time-consuming part of our business," says Fricot. "Almost immediately, our referral coordinator saw her end-to-end processing time for each referral drop by nearly 50 percent, which was huge for our offices. What used to take us up to two hours now takes five minutes. We are actually delivering patient care faster and minimizing re-work after the visit because we get accurate information up front. It's a win for everyone involved."

Electronic information has also brought more time for patient care and improved satisfaction for both staff and patients. "Before this information was made available electronically, our office staff spent upwards of an hour per patient getting all the necessary [health plan] benefits information. It was not unusual for a patient to arrive for an appointment and then have to call his or her insurance company trying to resolve plan coverage questions. Now, with so many health plans easily accessible in one place, we have all the information we need in seconds, and we rarely have to involve our patients in the process. It has made a tremendous improvement to patient and staff satisfaction," says Fricot.

Physician Revenue Management Consulting Company

As a revenue management consultant for multiple small physician practices in Florida, Merrilee Severino, CPC, CMM, CPM, has seen the incredible impact of electronic administrative tools using the multi-health plan network. "Many small practices would not be in business today if this didn't exist," she says.

Severino teaches one- and two-physician practices to use available information technology to simplify the administrative aspects of running a practice. "It's frustrating for a small practice when they don't have an easy way to get the information they need from health plans," says Severino. "They emphasize quality patient care, but when they can't get the information they need to manage the business, they don't get paid, and that has a negative impact on their ability to stay in business and help people get better."

Severino says that one of her past clients avoided bankruptcy because of the electronic access to health plans. "This provider was the victim of some fraudulent activity that left her in a negative cash flow situation. She had a number of bills that needed to be submitted to health plans and she could only afford one employee to help manage the business end of things."

In order to keep her practice running, the physician needed to be paid right away. With electronic access to eligibility and benefits, claim submission, and claim status, the patient cost estimator and online payment collection tools were the keys to keeping her in business. "We were able to eliminate days of work and get right to the information we needed to get her paid. She was able to get to cash flow positive in a matter of a couple of weeks. It really saved her business," says Severino.

The American Recovery and Reinvestment Act: Can the Reality Meet the Promise?

Into the midst of this kind of progress in the private sector comes the most massive government stimulus effort in our nation's history. As part of the *American Recovery and Reinvestment Act* (ARRA), signed into law in February 2009, the federal government will invest tens of billions of dollars to drive development, adoption, and the "meaningful use" of health IT to improve health outcomes. The bulk of this investment will go directly to providers. What we do not yet know is what we will get for this investment. That will ultimately be answered with red or black ink based upon how effectively the public and private sectors work together.

Providing financial incentives for physicians to adopt electronic health records is only part of the equation. For "meaningful use" to translate into broad physician adoption and utilization in the clinical workflow, the electronic health records systems must include meaningful clinical data, populated for the physician in real time during the patient encounter. Absent that, electronic health records, and thus ARRA funding, are merely empty vessels with tremendous promise but limited impact.

Thus, Availity has been aggressively promoting our view that the meaningful use criteria should specifically include administratively derived clinical information, or claims data, as a foundational component of the electronic health record. Aligning clinical and administrative information exchange makes tremendous sense. Administrative data is reliable, consistent, and readily available to be used for clinical decision support as a component of electronic health records. Further, as we are demonstrating in Florida through our collaboration with the Agency for Health Care Administration, the marriage of public and private sector administrative data, used for clinical decision support, can materially drive adoption and utilization of electronic health information.

Building upon the Administrative Foundation: The Future of Real-Time Information Exchange

The success of real-time administrative data exchange sets a firm foundation for a remarkable evolution in healthcare. While pockets of success are exciting and encouraging, widespread adoption is required to drive the change needed in the industry. Making this happen involves three key requirements from the stakeholder community:

1. **Collaboration.** Commercial and public sector health plans must come together as they have in Florida and a few other states to share data and utilize a common platform and portal.

2. **Commitment.** Health plans must be committed to supporting the platform through funding, marketing sponsorship, and continually enhancing the value of the information provided. Healthcare providers must be committed to utilizing the network as their de facto standard for health information exchange.

3. **Interoperability.** Everyone can agree to collaborate and be committed to a common solution, but if it is not interoperable, it will not be successful. The stakeholders must agree to use common standards for data exchange and communication.

As in building a house, wherein the walls and ceiling are only as strong as the foundation on which they reside, the promise of health information technology can be realized only by building on a solid infrastructure of administrative transactions. We know from decades of experience that sometimes to a physician even free is too expensive. For mass adoption to occur, providers must realize meaningful, profitable benefit in utilization of technology.

Providers will adopt technology—pagers, cell phones, BlackBerries, and the Web are just a few examples. They use these tools not because they were free but because they deliver value.

Health information technology is no different. Our experience in Florida shows that providers will use IT when they believe that it improves patient care, reduces inefficiencies, and enhances their practices. We must build upon our success and other successful models across the country so we can truly revolutionize both the delivery of care and its administration.

—⟋⟋⟍—

Julie D. Klapstein is the Chief Executive Officer of Availity, LLC, a joint venture of Blue Cross and Blue Shield of Florida, Inc., Health Care Service Corporation (HCSC), Humana Inc., and WellPoint, Inc. Availity optimizes information exchange among multiple healthcare stakeholders through a single, secure network. Since its inception in 2001, Availity has become one of the largest healthcare information networks in the country and has won 12 industry awards.

—⟋⟋⟍—

[1] National Automated Clearing House Association, *ACH 2007 Volumes*, May 19, 2008.

[2] U.S. Healthcare Efficiency Index, "U.S. Healthcare Efficiency Indext Fact Sheet," http://www.ushealthcareindex.com/resources/IndexFactSheet.pdf (accessed January 21, 2010).

[3] Nick A. LeCuyer and Shubham Singhal, "Overhauling the US Healthcare Payment System," *The McKinsey Quarterly*, June 2007.

[4] Manhattan Research, "Taking the Pulse," May 2009, http://www.ihealthbeat.org/Data-Points/2009/What-Percentage-of-Physicians-Report-That-the-Internet-Is-Essential-to-Their-Professional-Practice.aspx (accessed January 21, 2010).

[5] Michael W. Davis, "The State of U.S. Hospitals Relative to Achieving Meaningful Use Measures", *HIMSS Analytics 2009*, http://www.himssanalytics.org/docs/HA_ARRA_100509.pdf.

[6] "Electronic Transaction Savings Opportunities for Physician Practices," *Milliman* (January 2006). http://www.ushealthcareindex.com/resources/Milliman_EDI_Benefits.pdf.

[7] IBM Global Business Services, "CAQH CORE Phase I Measures of Success: Executive Summary and Industry-wide Savings Projection," (May 2009) http://www.caqh.org/pdf/COREIBMstudy.pdf (accessed January 21, 2010).

CHAPTER 8

Electronic Health Records and Clinical Research: A Timely Collision

Wyche "Tee" Green III and Jason Colquitt

—✺—

Editor's Introduction

In his international bestseller *Megatrends*, author John Naisbitt said, "We are drowning in information but starved for knowledge. This level of information is clearly impossible to be handled by present means. Uncontrolled and unorganized information is no longer a resource in an information society, instead it becomes the enemy."[1] While written nearly 30 years ago on the transformation into the information age, this passage perfectly captures today's healthcare system. We have more information on the human body than ever before, yet we know very little about how best to care for it. That is changing. With today's sophisticated technology, we have the ability to electronically capture, organize, and analyze discrete information. This information can be turned into powerful knowledge that can be used to promote health and wellness and to treat, cure, and prevent disease. Health information technology is the tool that will make this transformation a widespread reality.

—✺—

The promises of healthcare information technology, particularly electronic health records (EHRs), are many: improved quality, fewer medical errors, dramatic improvements in efficiency, and access to better care for more Americans. Many of these benefits are being realized today in hospitals and physician practices across the country. However, one profound benefit of modernizing healthcare through health IT has to be realized: the "collision" of EHRs with clinical research.

The 2007 book *Paper Kills* included a chapter on the power of data to advance research and clinical improvement. The introduction put it this way:

When medical data is turned into secure, actionable knowledge, money—and lives—are saved. Data can identify the sickest patients who need the most help; who is genetically predisposed for specific diseases and who is not; who are the best doctors and who are the worst; which treatments work and which do not; and other vital information. But today's healthcare system is not designed to deliver this kind of knowledge. Data is largely confined to paper medical records scattered across the spectrum of care, with virtually no way to aggregate it from all the disparate sources. As physicians, hospitals, and health plans embrace health information technology and begin to collect and securely share electronic data, we will have the ability to aggregate it and gain invaluable insights into community health, effective treatment regiments, compliance with clinical guidelines, and physician performance.[2]

The key to realizing such a future, in which technology transforms health and healthcare, is information. This starts with collecting the right data in a secure, efficient way that guarantees patient privacy. This data will support high-quality patient care as well as the essential research that advances the practice of medicine through clinical trials. Clinical trials are studies performed on patients after laboratory testing of new medications, combinations of medications, and surgical and radiotherapy procedures. Clinical trials are highly regulated and structured to ensure patient safety and valid results. According to the National Institutes of Health, there were more than 27,000 active clinical trials around the world in November 2009, with roughly half of those being conducted in the United States.[3] One of the biggest challenges is collecting valid clinical information.

Obstacles and Opportunities

Collecting data to support research and reporting activities has traditionally been a manual effort. Current data collection leaves many professionals, from health information management and IT to doctors and nurses, literally combing through paper records one by one. They then manually enter the needed information into simplistic software applications or spreadsheets, typically referred to as electronic data capture.

This laborious process, while an improvement over previous approaches, has numerous drawbacks. It is time- and labor-intensive, which is a recipe for mistakes. Transcribed data is always subject to errors, either in the transcriber's interpretation of handwritten notes or typographical mistakes. Manual data collection is not in real time. Data entry is often done in "batches," so the information may be entered days, weeks, or even months after patients were actually seen. Physicians and patients could miss opportunities in a clinical trial if information is not collected and known in a timely manner.

In many instances, particularly in academic medical centers, information is extracted from billing and other HIT systems. This kind of data is often fragmented and often limited in its utility because it focuses on high-level diagnosis and procedure coding, rather than more discrete data that is required for clinical research, public health reporting, and quality reporting.

Enter EHRs. EHRs can dramatically improve these processes, leading to more efficient, reliable, and timely data collection. Rather than paying a small army of professionals, EHRs can automate data collection. Instead of the risk of human error, EHRs can electronically capture patient data through medical devices. And rather than reporting data when an individual is ready to manually submit it, EHRs can report data in virtually real time or at regularly scheduled intervals.

These kinds of systems have been available for many years, and organizations from across the country have used information technology to dramatically improve the quality of care and its administration. Computerized provider order entry (CPOE), clinical documentation, electronic prescribing, and closed-loop medication management are all important components that generate and collect the kinds of discrete patient-level data needed to support population reporting and quality analyses.

American Recovery and Reinvestment Act

Unfortunately, those that have adopted EHRs and other information technologies are the exception, not the rule. One major barrier has been cost. To address this problem, the economic stimulus legislation, the *American Recovery and Reinvestment Act of 2009* (ARRA), made a substantial investment in moving physicians, nurses, and hospitals from paper to electronic systems. ARRA provides $30 billion in direct cash incentives to providers for the "meaningful use" of EHRs. That is, if providers adopt and use EHRs to meet certain quality-based criteria, including the collection and reporting of certain patient data, they will receive bonus payments from Medicare or Medicaid of up to $64,000 per physician.

Healthcare providers who adopt EHRs and hit the meaningful use criteria will be well positioned to extend the power and promise of these technologies to support clinical research and other data aggregation needs. In fact, the ARRA also invested in population-based research to better understand the efficacy and effectiveness of treatments, therapies, and other important information. This funding will be used to:

> ... conduct, support, or synthesize research that compares the clinical outcomes, effectiveness, and appropriateness of items, services, and procedures that are used to prevent, diagnose, or treat diseases, disorders, and other health conditions; and...encourage the development and use of clinical registries, clinical data networks, and other forms of electronic health data that can be used to generate or obtain outcomes data.[4]

This work will complement the strategy outlined by Dr. David Blumenthal, the National Coordinator for Health Information Technology. Speaking at a National Quality Forum conference in October 2009, Dr. Blumenthal emphasized that the ability of clinicians to collect, analyze, and report healthcare quality measures is crucial to his office's strategy for using IT to transform the U.S. healthcare system. "The key to meaningful use is to know how to measure for performance and to be able to give feedback to providers," Dr. Blumenthal said. The general objective is to convert existing quality measures into metrics that can be incorporated into EHRs in a standard form so they can be compared across practices and communities.

The federal investment in health IT will lead to an unprecedented demand for more efficient and accurate data collection tools, complex analyses, and secure dissemination of healthcare information. From more timely immunization registries, cancer registries, reporting on adverse drug events, and drug recalls to the dramatic time savings in testing new medications and treatments—clearly the time has come to apply EHR technology to the challenges of information management to support clinical research, public health, and quality initiatives.

From Today's Technology to Tomorrow's Research

Secondary uses of data collected in EHRs are not generally understood by all healthcare stakeholders. Among those who have studied these potential uses, there is a strong belief that this information can dramatically impact healthcare quality. Michael Ibara, PharmD, head of pharmacovigilance information management at Pfizer, has stated, "If we could capture the data from EHRs every time a doctor discontinues a drug along with the reason, and if that reason was for an if that reason was for an adverse drug event, we would immediately improve patient safety and drug surveillance in the U.S."[5]

Dr. Ibara coordinated the ASTER Project (Adverse Drug Event Spontaneous Triggered Event Reporting). Working in Boston, Massachusetts, with Brigham and Women's Hospital, Partners Healthcare, and leading quality and research groups, the project automated the data collection of adverse drug events in the EHR used in an ambulatory clinic. A flexible standard known as Retrieve Form for Data allowed for the direct importation of data into an electronic case report form, where the requisite reports were then sent electronically to the Food and Drug Administration (FDA).

This breakthrough work has demonstrated the value of automating the collection and reporting of adverse drug events. ASTER study participants present their work as a model for researchers, clinicians, HIT software providers, and other healthcare stakeholders who clearly see the broad adoption of EHRs as the opportunity to exploit these robust technologies across the healthcare delivery continuum.

Physician Participation in Clinical Trials

A key benefit of research-enabled EHRs is to aid physician and patient participation in clinical trials. These research studies obviously give patients access to the latest medical advances, but they also allow physicians the opportunity to generate additional income through study participation as well as enhance patient retention and satisfaction.

Despite these advantages, most physicians do not participate in clinical trials because of the effort required to identify and recruit patients, cull data from charts, and complete the reporting required by the FDA as well as the contract research organization. Such low participation by physicians means low participation among patients. Without the vital information of how well new treatments and therapies perform, it hampers the ability of researchers to expedite breakthroughs and cure diseases. The following chart from a 2009 FDA analysis of first-time participants in clinical trials shows that the number of studies is increasing faster than the number of physicians opting in.

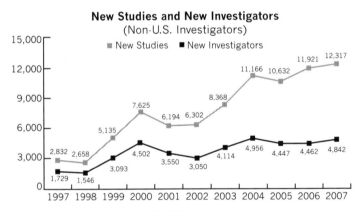

New Studies and New Investigators
(Non-U.S. Investigators)

Source: Centerwatch Analysis 2009, FDA

EHRs can help solve this problem. There are systems on the market today that can automate and streamline much of the data collection, but they can also allow physicians to better identify and recruit patients for clinical trials. With new financial incentives included in the economic stimulus legislation, even small physician practices will have tools to support their participation in these studies.

Take, for example, *PrimeResearch*®, a tool that can be integrated with Greenway Medical Technology's practice-based EHR, *Prime-Suite*. These two technologies can merge the day-to-day delivery of patient care with robust clinical research. *PrimeResearch*® is fully HIPAA compliant and can identify and collect patient data that is generated from providers' interactions with EHRs as they care for their patients. Once a clinical trial begins, the tool can identify patients who meet inclusion/exclusion criteria for feasibility. The physician is then notified of the opportunity and the number of candidate patients. Should the physician opt in, the physician will be electronically connected with the study sponsor. Once the study is under way, the research tool and the EHR work in conjunction to collect and report data for the study, auto-filling the required case report forms and sending them electronically to the necessary clinical research systems and regulatory entities such as the FDA.

The FDA estimates that it requires 36 minutes to fill out the MedWatch voluntary reporting form, including the time for reviewing instructions, searching existing data sources, gathering and maintaining the data needed, and completing and reviewing the collection of information.[6] Based on his experience with the ASTER project described above, Dr. Ibara of Pfizer stated at a July 2009 conference, "What used to take 36 minutes can now be done in less than a minute!"[7]

The automation required to complete MedWatch and clinical trial reporting forms was built into the *PrimeSuite* EHR by working with standards organizations, including the Clinical Data Interchange Standards Consortium (CDISC), Integrating the Healthcare Enterprise (IHE), and the Health Information Technology Standards Panel (HITSP). A key partner was Outcome Sciences, a contract research organization. This kind of partnership helps identify study protocols and participation criteria. This allows Greenway to pre-screen customer sites based on specialty and candidate patients who might qualify and to build tailored data forms based on the study's protocols. These can then be integrated into the EHRs of participating physicians for their participating patients, enabling the study's investigator to send the required data to the electronic data collection vendor from the EHR via pre-populated form.

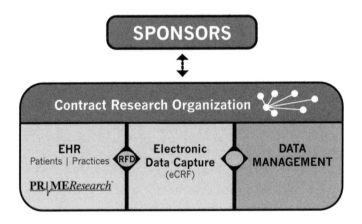

From Vision to Reality

There are a growing number of healthcare organizations that are embracing this approach. Professional Park Medical Services in Carrollton, Georgia, outside Atlanta, is a four-physician health-care practice that manages more than 25,000 patient visits a year. They have been using an electronic health record since 2005, and started working with *PrimeResearch Network* in 2008.

Physicians at Professional Park Medical participated in a clinical research study on pain management. Two hundred fifty patients who met the criteria were electronically identified and presented to clinicians as part of their normal workflow within the EHR. The only paper required was the consent form. Reporting require-ments are met through normal, everyday use of the EHR, so there is no additional administrative burden. This means that for the first time, due to minimal impact on workflow, participation in a research study makes business sense.

Sebastian Mason, LPN, of Professional Park Medical, has seen the enthusiasm of the physicians in his practice and the improve-ments for their patients who have access to new medications and treatments. According to Mr. Mason, "We didn't consider clinical research opportunities until we got involved with this project.

Now, 80 percent of the required data is automatically collected so the physician has only to respond to the subjective questions about patient's response to the protocol or why other meds were prescribed, for example." The group is now looking to evaluate patients with congestive heart failure to compare their protocols and their outcomes.

More and more physician practices and clinics are adopting integrated technology to use in clinical research, public health, and quality initiatives.

- Mound Family Practice Associates, a three-physician practice in Miamisburg, Ohio, uses *PrimeResearch* to support the Physician Quality Reporting Initiative (PQRI) data collection and reporting for increased Medicare reimbursement. They saw a 1.5 percent increase in Medicare revenues in 2008, and are on track to realize a 2 percent increase in 2009.
- Three practices are participating in test studies of women with abnormal uterine bleeding who are taking oral contraception: Oswego County OB/GYN, an eight-physician practice in New York; Omega OB/GYN Associations, a six-physician practice in South Arlington, Texas; and OB/GYN Associates of Alabama, a four-physician practice in Birmingham, Alabama. Their EHRs have identified 572 qualified patients across the three practices to work with the study sponsor, Nextrials.
- Seven additional practices, which care for nearly 385,000 patients, are participating in a study of patients with atrial fibrillation, working with Outcomes Sciences as the contract research organization.

These projects broaden the utility and value of EHRs to a wide range of practice settings. It brings clinical research opportunities to small practices so they can provide better care for their patients and communities. It also brings a wider spectrum of patients to researchers to both enhance their research validity and deliver new medical solutions to market faster. With few practicing physicians participating in research, this represents a new frontier.

What the Future Holds

This transformational work will generate tremendous interest as EHRs are more broadly adopted and as healthcare continues to evolve to be more efficient and effective. This collaboration among vendors, providers, and researchers will create a model that will transform both care delivery and clinical research. There remain, however, some challenges to overcome.

1. **Streamline work flows and clinical processes.** Work flows and clinical processes vary widely across healthcare delivery settings, depending on size, patient volume, specialty, and provider training. Data collection processes that support clinical research and other data aggregation activities are typically defined by FDA regulations, which are different from those that govern EHRs. The FDA has little experience with EHRs, so it is unlikely that the potential of these systems to support clinical research efforts is truly understood. These differences will need to be recognized and addressed to realize the full potential of EHRs to support clinical research, public health, and quality reporting.

2. **Standardize data.** Good progress on standards for healthcare information technology has been made in the past several years. However, standards for data sets and communications protocols in the areas of research, public health, and quality reporting must be better coordinated among participating stakeholders. More energy must be spent on implementing a single set of standards for interoperability between healthcare delivery organizations, public health, and clinical researchers.

3. **Provider education.** Physicians and other providers must be educated about the advantages of participating in clinical research. Few practice-based clinicians have experience in this area. But because these settings are where the majority of Americans receive care, they hold the greatest potential to benefit the healthcare system as a whole. This education might be provided by the Regional Extension Centers funded by ARRA.

4. **Regulation.** The current related regulations do not clearly consider the concept of electronic data capture applications.

Additional clarity at a regulatory level is needed to ensure that data reentry is not required and that maximum benefits are achieved from data interchange between electronic data capture and EHR systems. This is particularly important so that adoption is not discouraged for fear of the regulatory backlash if physicians choose to take advantage of EHR capabilities to support data aggregation activities. Current efforts to define "meaningful use" criteria might be bogged down by considering electronic data capture, but it should clearly be a priority going forward.

Conclusion

The widespread integration of workflow-based information technology with cutting-edge clinical research has the power to transform care delivery and patient health. The more we know about chronic disease and the more we understand how treatments and therapies work, the better we can begin to reverse the troubling trends in population health and find the cures to diseases like Alzheimer's and cancer. It is only through empowering patients and their doctors with the information and research opportunities can we make this a reality. We are on the cusp of enormous change, and these kinds of exciting innovations will most assuredly play an essential role.

—⁂—

Wyche "Tee" Green III is the President of Greenway Medical Technologies and is responsible for leading the company's strategic direction while managing day-to-day operations. Greenway Medical Technologies provides solutions and on-demand services for physician practices, hospitals, IDNs, RHIOs, and IPAs and has been named one of Deloitte's Georgia Fast 50 and national Fast 500.

Jason Colquitt is the Director of Research and Outcomes for Greenway Medical Technologies. He leads the strategic implementation of standards and interoperability for Greenway's range of clinical, practice management, and financial solutions. Mr. Colquitt has led key divisions through the developmental milestones of the company's integrated physician infrastructure.

—m—

[1] John Naisbitt, *Megatrends* (New York: Warner Books, 1982).

[2] David Merritt. *Paper Kills*. (Washington, D.C.: CHT Press, 2007), 133.

[3] ClinicalTrials.gov, http://www.clinicaltrials.gov (accessed January 21, 2010).

[4] *American Recovery and Reinvestment Act of 2009*, H.R.1, p. 63.

[5] "Aster: A Collaborative Study to Improve Drug Safety," http://www.asterstudy.com/index.php?option=com_content&view=article&id=10:aster-description (accessed January 25, 2010).

[6] MedWatch, http://www.fda.gov/downloads/aboutFDA/CentersOffices/CDER/ucm103109.pdf (accessed on January 20, 2010).

[7] "Aster: A Collaborative Study to Improve Drug Safety," http://www.asterstudy.com/index.php?option=com_content&view=article&id=10:aster-description (accessed January 25, 2010).

CHAPTER 9

An Open Invitation: Melding Open-Source Software and Technological Innovation

Robert M. Barthelmes and Timothy M. Elwell

—⚡—

Editor's Introduction

In Tom Friedman's book *The World Is Flat*, he tells the story of an IBM executive who was in the battle for supremacy of e-commerce during the early years of the Internet.[1] When told that Web servers ran on software created by an informal network of volunteer programmers and available for free, he didn't get it. Who runs it? How do you buy it? Who supports it if something goes wrong? "I mean, who are these guys?" Welcome to open-source software. Open source differs from proprietary software because the programming code—the recipe for how it runs—is in the public domain. Anyone can access, modify, and use it. This approach is slowly making its way into healthcare, especially with health information exchange, because it is free, flexible, and adaptive. Just as it did for the Internet, open source has the powerful potential to drive connectivity and innovation and should be an important part of modernizing our health system.

—⚡—

It is time to blow up what we are doing. We can look at almost any other industry and see examples of innovation resulting in transformational improvements in products, delivery of service, and business models. That is the challenge for healthcare IT.

> Steve O'Neill
> Chief Information Officer
> Hartford Hospital

Hartford Hospital, an urban hospital in the middle of a large indigent population, became quite adept at doing more with less and leveraging innovation in their IT shop to improve their care delivery systems. Using an acquisitive business model and a combination of good vision, good staff, and an eye to open-source communities, Hartford succeeds in areas where others have failed. Indeed, Hartford is the driver behind what may grow to be the first statewide open-source health information network in the United States.

This chapter takes a closer look at how the health information exchange (HIE) market has a chance to get it right in healthcare. The chapter explains how and why concepts like the free economy, the Internet platform for innovation, open-source software, and open-community collaboration as a design strategy can and will transform the industry. That is what is happening in Connecticut, where vendor-supported open software development is providing open innovation to Hartford Hospital and the creation of the Connecticut HIE.

New Normal

Over the past year, everyone has had to quickly adjust to what Roger McNamee has labeled the "new normal." The term is used to characterize the collective impact of changes that have suddenly altered our lifestyle, along with an acknowledgement that we are never going to go back to where we once were. In the economic downturn, individuals and businesses tightened their belts, but the urgency of the situation also forced businesses to forget about the past and to reevaluate existing practices going forward. To survive the new normal, McNamee advises, "The trick is to get real about the new set of challenges we face, and if you're willing to be a little different from everyone else, there are countless opportunities worth pursuing."[2]

In the business of healthcare, reality may be finally hitting home. If we ever expect to have a chance of rectifying common problems that continue to hamper progress and market growth (such as the lack of interoperability), members of the healthcare software industry need to work openly and collaboratively in pursuit of freely available solutions. We need to understand and join the new reality: open-source software is dominating IT infrastructures, the free economy is defining new business models, technology is being completely interwoven into our social fabric, and business strategies are about creating value and not just capturing customers and market share.

Free: The New Economy

In the early 1990s, when the Internet was bursting onto the scene, a common question was, "Who owns the Internet?" The answer, of course, was no one and everyone. That concept was difficult for most businesspeople and users to comprehend. It ran contrary to conventional thinking of a customer and user base that was accustomed to paying for everything. The ballgame changed forever with Tim Berners-Lee's invention of the Web browser, followed by Marc Andreessen's free distribution of the commercial Netscape browser. Suddenly the network (i.e., the Internet) became the great enabler. Users could freely access and exchange the most important asset, information, in ways never imagined with an easy-to-use interface and no special software. Few would argue that the Internet has been history's biggest boon to free enterprise—more than any other single technology. And think about this: it's *free*!

As users became exposed to the concept of what Chris Anderson of *Wired* magazine labeled the "free economy," it was not long before users concluded, "Why pay for content that I can get for nothing?"[3] Quickly, free to the user has become an expectation, like finding free Wi-Fi in every coffee shop. But recall Milton Friedman's famous line, "There is no such thing as a free lunch." Nothing is actually free. Revenues just need to come from someplace else.

Open Source Runs the Free Economy

The foundation of the Internet was developed with technology that anyone can use and no one has to pay for. It is the open-source movement personified. In its purest form, open source is a software development and distribution method that is characterized by relaxed intellectual property restrictions. Open-source contributors (an earned position in open-source communities) share know-how and documentation so that other developers with reasonable experience can understand the software and reuse or improve it. The reach of open-source communities and the power of the peer-review process often results in the production of quality code that far exceeds what any individual company could imagine accomplishing within its corporate domain.

With open source, the term "free" is used to refer to the developer's freedom to use the code and embellish it—the freedom to work within the community or outside the community if desired and the freedom to incrementally improve the code in order to meet an objective. Although open-source software may be provided at zero or little cost, open source is about the collaborative development of software that has business implications. Open source has become the free market response to the restrictions and cost consequences often imposed by proprietary software.

Open-Source Acceptance

Following the financial crisis in the early 1990s, open-source alternatives, such as Linux, gathered greater consideration as options and eventually gained traction. As we deal with the current financial downturn and the pressure on IT budgets, similar economic pressure is being felt, and it is not surprising that companies and U.S. government agencies have taken a heightened interest in cost-effective technologies like open source. After years of improvements, Linux is now installed in the vast majority of the world's 500 fastest supercomputers.

Open source has made significant inroads at the system and infrastructure level. Amazon, for example, has adopted open-source infrastructure and operating system components, resulting in millions of dollars in savings on a consistent yearly basis. Additionally, 30 percent of Amazon's revenues come from third-party sellers using its open platform for e-commerce. At the same time, the Amazon platform and application services (e.g., buying books) remain proprietary. This mixing of commercial and open-source modules to construct an application system is now the norm.

**Open Source in Mixed Hybrid Environments:
An Evolving Model**

Open source has become an integral part of modern software design, and commercial software providers are increasingly developing solutions that are a hybrid mix of open source and proprietary components. Saugatuck Research states, "Mixed-source software that incorporates open source to reduce development costs and improve user adoption will become a dominant industry trend. And by 2011, more than half of their key on-premise software will be open source."[4] One example of how the federal government is actively encouraging the development of open-source software is in the creation of the nationwide health information network (NHIN).

Hybrid technical configurations combine the very best qualities of proprietary and open-source software while supporting a business model that melds the open-source concepts of collaboration, community, and transparency with the commercial services and support structure of proprietary software. In this model, commercial providers utilize available open-source software components but retain ownership of proprietary portions that provide unique value to the vendor's solution. Utilizing open-source code and the type of licensing terms that are employed provides the commercial vendor with more latitude in pricing. For this reason, it is not surprising that Gartner predicts, "By 2012, more than 90 percent of enterprises will use open source in direct or embedded forms."[5]

Open Source and Meaningful Disruption

As open source moves beyond system-level software and into the application space, it is likely to create fear among software companies that an attack is in progress on traditional software licensing revenues. At Misys this has already happened. The interesting twist on this theme is that Misys CEO Mike Lawrie introduced the threat to the rest of the company by creating an open-source division inside his traditional proprietary software company. His premise was that in order to successfully turn the company around, he needed to introduce "meaningful disruption." There may be nothing more disruptive inside a traditional proprietary software company than open source. As Don Tapscott reminds us in his book *Wikinomics*, when referencing commercial software providers, "Commercial success of their products increases their dependency on them" and as a result, "entrenched industry players are generally not motivated to develop or deploy disruptive technologies."[6]

Why is open source so disruptive? The short answer is that it addresses and resolves many of the challenges of closed, proprietary technology and vendors. There is no "vendor lock-in." Open source allows users to connect with the technologies and systems of their choosing, working toward true interoperability, rather than being siloed with one system or vendor. Often, open source frees users from annual licensing fees, subscription charges, and upgrades and schedules determined by others. In short, open source is a liberator.

Electronic Medical Records and Health Information Exchanges: Value Proposition?

In 2004, President George W. Bush launched an electronic health record initiative with the goal of establishing EHRs for all Americans within 10 years. Upon signing the *American Recovery and Reinvestment Act*, President Barack Obama upped the ante and committed the nation to provide all citizens with an EHR by 2014. A part of the stimulus bill referred to as the HITECH Act includes incentives for providers to install and "meaningfully use" health information technology. The definitions of "meaningful use" will not be finalized until 2010, but one of the requirements will be that all the EHRs must have the ability to exchange and receive patient information from disparate source systems.

Despite the national attention paid to electronic health records, the adoption rate to date has been slow at best—17 percent of physician offices, according to an April 2009 study published in the *New England Journal of Medicine*.[7] Unfortunately, most physicians' offices are small businesses that have difficulty justifying the total cost of implementing EHRs. And when one factors in the issue of the immature regional health information networks and the problems ensuing from the lack of interoperability, the value proposition simply is not there for many.

What needs to happen? The sharing of patient information is a vital and missing function that logically cannot be addressed without an operational health information exchange (HIE). It is also generally understood that the HIE needs to attain a critical mass of useful services and users so that interconnectivity among providers will become apparent to other prospective providers and accelerate expansion. Growth will then drive exponential value which is not actualized today. So it is obvious that getting HIEs up and running must be a top priority, but they can be very expensive.

What to do? How can software vendors drive down costs? One possible way to drive down HIE costs and attain greater flexibility is to use open-source software, allowing software vendors to act creatively and collaboratively, not independently, to develop common HIE infrastructure components.

Platform for Innovation

The interconnected network of HIEs and the NHIN is destined to become the next biggest technological innovation for healthcare. Once the open platform for sharing patient information is functional, the network will quickly transform into an enabler for innovation. Instead of trying to make their fortunes designing and implementing proprietary HIEs, software providers should be more interested in collaborating in the creation of an open platform, so they can sell applications that easily plug into a standard framework.

It is not difficult to recognize the success of the Apple iPhone, which is not open source, but provides an open and enabling platform for innovation. At last report, more than 100,000 applications have been developed. Healthcare technology can benefit from enabling platforms, also being developed as "Platform-as-a-Service," that host offerings supporting meaningful use services. We simply need to follow the money.

A carefully considered open-source strategy finds a way to introduce various revenue streams that are annuity-based. For instance, in an HIE, in which the interoperability components are open source, one model could give the exchange and the portal away for free and charge only for those services that deliver value to the end user. In the Misys Open Source Solutions HIE product strategy, we provide the underlying open-source exchange platform for "free" but charge a subscription fee for value-added components that are accessible through the portal, such as e-prescribing, referrals management, lab routing, transcription services, secure messaging, and encounter management. All these services provide immediate return to the providers and give them a reason to use the exchange. There is no up-front payment, and they pay only for what they use.

Business Strategy: Hartford Works with Misys Open Source Solutions

Early in 2009, members of the Hartford Hospital were already engaged in the in-house design of an HIE infrastructure utilizing open-source components. As part of their investigation of the open-source community, the Hartford IT staff discovered that Misys Open Source Solutions (MOSS) was pursuing a similar open-source strategy and had already developed key components that Hartford needed. Collaborating openly as part of a Hartford project, Hartford and Misys Open Source Solutions worked together to finish the remaining components that were needed to run an HIE.

The pragmatism of the approach began to attract the attention of other large physician groups and other hospitals in the region that recognized the need but did not have the technical capability to get an exchange off the ground. Within three months of beginning the project with Misys and after a few demonstrations of the technology, Steve O'Neill, Chief Information Officer at Hartford Hospital, was able to attract the interest of some 20 of 34 hospitals in Connecticut to support the initiative, including Yale-New Haven. Mr. O'Neill, with the backing of the majority of Connecticut-based hospitals, created an exchange consortium primarily composed of Connecticut hospitals, competitive and friendly, that was referred to as Transforming Healthcare in Connecticut Communities (THICC) and worked in earnest with the consulting team from Misys to create a governance model to support the THICC mission to build out a statewide exchange.

Mr. O'Neill's efforts soon attracted the attention of eHealth Connecticut (eHCT), the original Connecticut-based regional health information organization (RHIO) that had been organized a few years earlier. eHCT had been successful in attracting investment from the Department of Social Services (DSS) in the state and as a result had begun to aggregate consumer advocate groups to support important policy documents. However, eHCT was not successful in building out a technology infrastructure that was needed to satisfy the DSS requirements for continued funding.

The respective boards of THICC and eHCT realized that apart, their efforts would not be as strong as a combined initiative that could leverage the relationships that eHCT had built at the state level and the advanced technology and hospital support that THICC brought to the table. However, before eHCT would agree to a merger of the boards, it demanded a demonstration of the THICC technology. Shrewdly, eHCT required that the MOSS technology platform meet an important milestone that DSS was expecting from eHCT. That milestone included the ability of the exchange to identify patients uniquely across a community of disparate hospitals and then locate documents associated with each patient, and display the standardized documents (Continuity of Care Documents or CCDs) in a common, browser-based portal with no special software required at the user's location.

MOSS easily met this requirement using an open source platform based on the Integrating the Healthcare Enterprise profiles. These were the same profiles that the federal government has mandated in building out the NHIN. These profiles were recommended by the Office of the National Coordinator, which holds discretionary control over $2 billion in the HITECH Act to support the build-out of HIEs and the promotion of HIT nationwide.

The success of the first demonstration for eHCT led to the merging of the THICC and eHCT boards. The success also accelerated the need to provide robust auditing capabilities, role-based portal access, and additional application capabilities. Taking a chapter from the iPhone platform success, the proprietary MOSS services-based architecture that sits on top of the open-source exchange platform enabled other advanced applications to be made available to the users. To demonstrate the power of the approach, the Hartford Hospital project manager, John Destefano, reached out to InSite One, a Connecticut-based radiological imaging and archiving company, to exchange radiologic images inside the MOSS portal. If the portal could identify patients and their discharge summaries from different hospitals, there was no reason they could not exchange images. So the next board demonstration included the exchange of documents and images and provided roles-based access—something that InSite One was unable to do before. MOSS also demonstrated its ability to route lab results. The development began to catch on fire, and the users were the recipients of the innovation.

Today, MOSS is working on building out revenue-sharing business development relationships to add electronic prescribing, referral management, secure messaging, encounters management, billing services, and transcription services to its set of service offerings. Thinking of providing services at the point of aggregation instead of just from the edge is quite liberating. At MOSS, we refer to the value-added components as "clinical groupware." The model is clearly an example of what can work in healthcare if there is an opportunity to open the aperture and work collaboratively. And it all started by using an open-source platform.

Mr. O'Neill said it best when asked why the HIE is so important to Hartford Hospital and its community:

> The HIE provides infrastructure as services, patient information that physicians and hospitals can access needing only a Web browser and authorized credentials. The existence of the HIE presents us with the opportunity to demonstrate two things: patient information sharing and new ways of managing care.
>
> I like to think of the HIE in the same way that I think of the Internet. It provides a standards-based platform that allows users to easily and securely connect, communicate and exchange data in a timely and accurate manner. Like the Internet, the HIE infrastructure will provide developers with the backbone upon which to invent new applications that will furnish users (providers and patients) with capabilities that today they couldn't even imagine.

The Misys solution will be the first total open-source HIE stack in the United States. The Hartford solution will go live in the first quarter of 2010. The first services to be operational will include the ability to exchange documents (discharge summaries from hospitals and patient medical summaries from EHRs), electronically prescribe medications, and receive and route lab orders.

Conclusion

The healthcare industry has not been successful in promoting the adoption of HIT thus far, and our current course will never solve it. While providers of care wait for the right technology delivered by the right business model, our current healthcare system will continue to spend too much money and claim too many lives. Any innovation that increases the probability for success needs to be supported and encouraged. Open source is an example of a disruptive change that is ready for prime time. It needs to be given the consideration of buyers and vendors.

The Misys Open Source Solutions group has adopted a quote that appears at the end of each e-mail that is sent out. It is meant to remind the group and those the group works with that purposeful innovation is hard and that disruptive innovation may be viewed as a threat.

"First they ignore you, then they laugh at you, then they fight you, then you win."

—Mahatma Gandhi

Although the Misys open-source platform model is new, it has received unprecedented attention and has given us customer opportuntities that would have been impossibe for a purely proprietary vendor. To date, the Misys group has experienced each phase of the Gandhi prediction. But in the end, we will not be the true winners. With better care at lower costs, the American people will be.

—⟋⟍—

Robert M. Barthelmes is the Executive Vice President and General Manager of Misys Open Source Solutions, a division of Misys that shares open source technology to lead in the development of innovative customer solutions for healthcare and the environment.

Timothy M. Elwell is the Vice President of Misys Open Source Solutions, helping to expand the influence of the open source approach to improve patient care. Mr. Elwell leads the company's open source strategy in support of healthcare products and services offerings.

—⚏—

[1] Thomas Friedman, *The World Is Flat: A Brief History of the Twenty-first Century*, (New York: Farrar, Straus and Giroux, 2005).

[2] Roger McNamee and David Diamond, *The New Normal: Great Opportunities in a Time of Great Risk* (New York: Portfolio Hardcover, 2004).

[3] Chris Anderson, "Free! Why $0.00 Is the Future of Business," *Wired Magazine*, February 2008. http://www.wired.com/techbiz/it/magazine/16-03/ff_free.

[4] "Open Source Software: The Next Disruptive IT Influence," *Saugatuck Technology*, October 2007, http://www.saugatech.com/395order.htm.

[5] "The State of Open Source 2008," *Gartner Report*, April 2008.

[6] Don Tapscott and Anthony D. Williams, *Wikinomics: How Mass Collaboration Changes Everything* (New York: Penguin Group, 2006.)

[7] David Blumenthal, "Stimulating the Adoption of Health Information Technology," *New England Journal of Medicine*.

CHAPTER 10

Paperless Prescriptions:
The E-Prescribing Revolution to Improve Healthcare Quality and Lower Costs

Kate Berry

—⚕︎—

Editor's Introduction

Doctors and nurses write billions of prescriptions every year by hand. Unfortunately, this cumbersome, paper-based process costs billions of dollars and, more importantly, costs many lives. Electronic prescribing is a better way. It is safer, more efficient, and faster. In fact, the benefits of e-prescribing are so compelling that the Institute of Medicine called for all prescriptions to be written electronically by 2010. While we will not make that goal, we are making good progress. We will soon have a 21st-century model in which, after visiting with a patient and determining a necessary remedy, a doctor or nurse can, with only a few clicks of a mouse or through a handheld device, send a prescription to the local pharmacy. That should be the rule and not the exception. This change is not easy, but by working in concert, public and private stakeholders can make this a reality.

—⚕︎—

Handwritten prescriptions have been a standard practice for hundreds of years. But in the 21st century, the process of writing and manually administering prescriptions is a dinosaur, and a dangerous and costly one at that. This archaic approach to prescribing means that physicians and other prescribers must base their decisions on possibly inaccurate and incomplete information. The physician, for instance, must rely on paper records, his or her own memory, and that of the patient. In turn, the pharmacist must try to read handwritten or faxed prescriptions and interpret the prescriber's intentions. How can we possibly expect a safe, cost-effective, or quality outcome?

The tremendous volume and increasing complexity of prescriptions hinders the safety, efficiency, and effectiveness of paper prescribing. According to the National Association of Chain Drug Stores (NACDS), more than 3.5 billion prescriptions were dispensed in 2008.[1] According to the Institute of Medicine, more than 7,000 preventable deaths and an estimated 1.5 million preventable medication errors occur each year.[2] These numbers are unacceptable.

According to NACDS, there are 130 million Americans living with a chronic condition such as diabetes, asthma, hypertension, and/or heart disease. These conditions account for more than 50 percent of all prescriptions. The adherence rate across all conditions averages only 50 percent, meaning that patients follow their doctor's orders and take their medication only half the time. For these patients, their health and quality of life suffers, and there are few tools available in a paper prescribing world to fix this dangerous problem.

Paper prescribing is not only unsafe; it is costly, inefficient, and burdensome. The Institute for Safe Medication Practices reports that many errors result from miscommunication due to illegible handwriting, confusing abbreviations and dose designations, unclear telephone or verbal orders, ambiguous orders, and fax-related problems. Hundreds of millions of phone calls and faxes go back and forth between physician offices and pharmacies each year to clarify prescription-related information and to authorize prescription renewals. This failure can result in delays in patients getting much-needed medications.

Technology exists today that can solve these problems. Electronic prescribing automates the current manual processes that plague the system and creates safer, more effective ways to manage prescriptions and patient care.

Defining E-Prescribing

The Centers for Medicare and Medicaid Services (CMS) defines e-prescribing as "the transmission, using electronic media, of prescription or prescription-related information between a prescriber, dispenser, pharmacy benefit manager, or health plan, either directly or through an intermediary, including an e-prescribing network. E-prescribing includes, but is not limited to, two-way transmissions between the point of care and the dispenser."[3]

It is critical to emphasize that e-prescribing is also at the core of modernizing care with electronic health records. *The American Recovery and Reinvestment Act of 2009* will invest tens of billions of dollars to encourage the adoption and "meaningful use" of EHRs among physicians and hospitals. Beginning in 2011, the federal government will make financial incentives available to physicians caring for both Medicare and Medicaid patients based on certain criteria or "meaningful use" of EHRs. In June 2009, the Health Information Technology (HIT) Policy Committee, an advisory arm of the National Coordinator for Health Information Technology, proposed that e-prescribing be included as a core measure in this definition.

More specifically, the HIT Policy Committee proposed that electronic health records must encompass a fully informed, connected, and interoperable medication management process in which a prescriber uses a computer, handheld device, or other hardware with software that allows him or her to:

- Electronically access information regarding a patient's drug benefit coverage and prescription history;
- Electronically transmit the prescription to the patient's choice of pharmacy;
- Receive an electronic prescription renewal request from a pharmacist for approval; and,
- Support the entire medication management process on behalf of patients and each stakeholder in the process (i.e., prescribe, send, dispense, administer, and monitor).

Benefits of E-Prescribing by Stakeholder

Why will "meaningful use" of health information technology include e-prescribing? Why build from this foundation? Simply put: e-prescribing benefits every stakeholder in the medication management process and can improve the safety, quality, efficiency, and effectiveness of medication management.

According to the Center for Information Technology Leadership, e-prescribing with clinical decision support and bi-directional pharmacy connectivity can reduce adverse drug events by more than 60 percent compared to pen and paper.[4] A Gorman Health Group study indicated that approximately 70 percent of the safety and cost savings advantages of e-prescribing result from physicians accessing patient medication histories, safety alerts, preferred medication options, and pharmacy benefit information at the time of prescribing so they can make more informed decisions for their patients.[5]

An Agency for Healthcare Research and Quality study found that e-prescribing with formulary and decision support that allows physicians to select lower-cost or generic medications can save $845,000 per 100,000 patients and could reduce prescription drug spending by up to $3.9 million per 100,000 patients per year.[6]

E-prescribing is an important platform to enable payers to communicate formulary alerts, safety alerts, adherence reminders, and gaps in care alerts to prescribers. It also enables payers to communicate condition and therapy education, medication adherence education, and care reminders to patients.

One study showed that e-prescribing/EMR clinical decision support applications can lower the use of antibiotics by 18 percent, with an associated 26 percent decrease in infection rates. The same study also offered additional proof that if physicians are alerted appropriately by EHRs they generally do the right thing.[7]

Patients
Patients like e-prescribing because it gives them confidence that their physician is using state-of-the-art technology that will produce an accurate, readable prescription. They appreciate the convenience of fewer trips to the pharmacy and the reduction in costs. After all, e-prescribing facilitates conversation between physicians and patients about the cost of medications. Given the prescription benefit and formulary information, e-prescribing allows physicians and patients to make personalized decisions that may help the patient save money.

While this opportunity has only begun to be tested and explored, e-prescribing has tremendous potential to improve medication adherence and improve outcomes for many patients across the country. For example, because e-prescribing enables the physician to view the patient's medication history during the patient encounter, the physician may notice that the patient is refilling a prescription to treat a chronic condition every 45 days rather than every 30 days and may choose to remind the patient of the importance of taking the medication as prescribed. E-prescribing with patient medication history as a platform can also support messaging among the pharmacist, physician, and patient to remind the patient to pick up and take the medication as prescribed. In summary, e-prescribing offers better information and connectivity to enable personalized messaging that can help improve medication adherence.

Physicians
Physicians and other prescribers benefit from e-prescribing because they have better access to information and clinical decision support at the time of prescribing. They also have better documentation of the patient's prescriptions that can be accessed remotely. This means that if a physician is out of the office and receives a call that a patient needs a prescription, he can check the patient's record remotely to make sure the patient is not on another medication and does not have an allergy that might cause a drug-drug or drug-allergy interaction and can also be sure to prescribe a medication that is covered by the patient's drug benefit. Without e-prescribing, this level of safety and cost information would not be available to the physician without checking the patient's paper chart, and even then the information would be limited. Further, physicians and their staff benefit from the reduction in phone calls from pharmacies to clarify prescription information. E-prescribing also streamlines the process by reducing faxes and phone calls associated with authorizing prescription renewals, saving several hours per day.

Payers and PBMs
Payers and pharmacy benefit managers (PBM) experience cost savings with e-prescribing because of improved formulary compliance and an increased use of generic medications and other lower-cost

alternatives. IMS Health has estimated that a 1 percent increase in generic utilization would yield almost $4 billion in savings.[8] There are also cost savings associated with the avoidance of adverse drug events, emergency visits, hospitalizations, and doctor visits.

Pharmacies
Pharmacies benefit from e-prescribing in many ways: it improves patient service, reduces errors due to misinterpretation, avoids delays of treatment due to missing information, saves time by substantially reducing calls and faxes to clarify information or to request authorization or prescription renewals, and minimizes rework and data entry.

E-Prescribing Adoption

The adoption of e-prescribing has come a long way in recent years. More than 85 percent of the nation's community pharmacies and many of the major mail-order pharmacies are e-prescribing. According to our network traffic, as of December 2009, there were more than 155,000 physicians and other prescribers using e-prescribing, which amounts to about 25 percent of office-based physicians. More than 70 percent of the 155,000 active e-prescribers are using electronic health records. About 15 percent of eligible prescriptions are being generated and sent electronically.

Prescription benefit, formulary, and prescription history information is available for more than 220 million Americans through Surescripts, which operates a nationwide network built by the nation's pharmacies and leading PBMs. The network allows payers and PBMs to share prescription benefit information with physicians and other prescribers that use certified e-prescribing and electronic health record systems. This national infrastructure makes available prescription history information to physician offices, acute care facilities, and health information exchanges. It also facilitates the routing of prescriptions between physician offices and community and mail-order pharmacies nationwide.

One of the keys behind the growth of e-prescribing in the United States is the neutrality of the nation's network. Surescripts does not own, sell, or promote software, thereby affording prescribers a wide choice of software offered by 250+ technology vendors. The same neutrality principle prohibits commercial messaging of any kind during the time of prescribing by Surescripts certified systems. This protects a patient's choice of pharmacy and a physician's choice of medication therapy.

Beyond operating a neutral network, Surescripts also leads multiple industry-wide initiatives focused on the development, implementation, and enhancement of national standards, workflow enhancements, and best practices for e-prescribing. This critical work ensures that all of the hundreds of software vendors and participants across the network are certified and compliant with a consistent set of requirements to enable industry-wide interoperability and exchange of medication information.

The growth in electronic prescribing has accelerated rapidly, and the trend is likely to continue. At the end of 2006, there were 16,000 active e-prescribing physicians—an almost tenfold increase in three years. Similar progress has been made across multiple fronts: information is available on more patients through e-prescribing by connecting payers and PBMs; more technology vendors have brought e-prescribing solutions to the marketplace; and independent pharmacies are increasing their use. All this progress means that the national e-prescribing infrastructure is robust and that many payers, PBMs, physicians, pharmacies, and patients are realizing the benefits of this lifesaving technology.

E-Prescribing Champions

There are many important drivers of e-prescribing. The public sector has been leading, with federal and state policymakers taking critical steps to advance e-prescribing. In addition to the *American Recovery and Reinvestment Act*, starting in January 2009, CMS put into effect the Medicare Improvements for Patients and Providers Act (MIPPA) to offer financial incentives for eligible professionals to adopt a qualified e-prescribing system. For those who do not adopt it, penalties are expected to apply in 2012. In the second half of 2008 after MIPAA was announced, e-prescribing adoption began to accelerate rapidly, particularly among large health systems and medical groups that were organized and focused on optimizing incentive payments for their affiliated physicians by supporting them in adopting e-prescribing. Physicians who take care of a large proportion of Medicare patients, such as ophthalmologists, became very focused on adopting e-prescribing in order to get their incentive payments under MIPAA.

The private sector and many public-private partnerships have also been critical in driving the progress of e-prescribing. Across the country, many health plans, health systems, medical groups, governors' offices, state departments of health, and multi-stakeholder collaborative groups have worked hard to encourage adoption and use of e-prescribing.

Rhode Island and Vermont
There are many examples of e-prescribing at the state level, but Rhode Island and Vermont illustrate the largest trend.

Rhode Island, the first state to implement e-prescribing through Surescripts in early 2004, recently announced that it was the first state to reach the goal of 100 percent e-prescribing by pharmacies. Today, 31 percent of all prescriptions are now generated and sent electronically within the state. In addition, Surescripts and the state's pharmacies are providing epidemiologists at the Rhode Island Department of Health with weekly reports of de-identified prescription data for disease surveillance, specifically monitoring and tracking the use of antiviral prescribing data during the H1N1 pandemic. This provides another important tool for the state's public health officials to look at trends related to the course, severity, and treatment of H1N1.

Recently, the state of Vermont received a $1 million grant to jump-start e-prescribing. Vermont Information Technology Leaders is a non-profit that operates as a public-private partnership to expand the use of health information technology and make e-prescribing software available to physicians practicing in the state. The program will also provide financial incentives to forty independent pharmacies in Vermont to begin e-prescribing.

In order to raise awareness among states about their performance with e-prescribing, Surescripts created the Safe-Rx program, which ranks states based on their use of e-prescribing. In 2009, the Safe-Rx Awards were co-hosted by Tennessee governor Phil Bredesen and Vermont governor Jim Douglas, who co-chaired the National Governors Association's State Alliance for eHealth. The program highlights the growth of e-prescribing at the state and national levels. Going forward, the state ranking system will evolve to capture key aspects of meaningful use, including the use of prescription benefits, prescription history, and prescription routing.

At the national level, 15 medical societies joined with the Center for Improving Medication Management to launch the Get Connected program.[9] Get Connected is a web-based program that offers education, tools, and resources to assist physician offices in moving toward e-prescribing. The program is widely promoted by medical societies.

eHealth Initiative, the Center for Improving Medication Management, the American Medical Association, the American Academy of Family Physicians, the Medical Group Management Association, and the American College of Physicians developed *A Clinician's Guide to E-Prescribing*, which was released in October 2008 at the CMS E-Prescribing Conference in Boston. This document is a leading resource for physicians and other prescribers who are seeking information on why e-prescribing is important, how it works, how to get started, and how to implement it successfully.[10]

E-Prescribing Barriers and Challenges

Despite the progress of the past few years and the enormous potential on the horizon, challenges to widespread adoption of e-prescribing remain.

Controlled Substances
While thousands of prescriptions can be written and transmitted electronically, the Drug Enforcement Administration (DEA) prohibits the electronic transmission of prescriptions for controlled substances, such as Vicodin or oxycontin. For physicians and other prescribers, this creates an obvious barrier to their use of e-prescribing, since according to NACDS, in 2008, more than 350 million prescriptions—about 10 percent of all prescriptions— were written for controlled substances. Stakeholders across the

healthcare industy are continuing to work with the DEA to pass regulations that allow controlled substances to be electronically prescribed in a manner that is both workable and scalable and balances the legitimate and important interests of law enforcement, private industry, and federal and state governments.

Cost
Cost is also frequently cited as a barrier to physician adoption of e-prescribing and electronic health records. The substantial incentives coming from the stimulus legislation and MIPPA to drive physician adoption can help allay this concern.

Workflow Disruptions
In the transition to e-prescribing, physician offices and, to some extent, pharmacies can experience significant challenges related to workflow and management. It can be difficult to make the transition from paper to electronic prescribing. Physician practices must ensure adequate time for training and support; otherwise they will struggle and not take full advantage of the benefits of e-prescribing.

It is often difficult to find answers when physician practices run into technical or workflow challenges and confusion and misinformation arise about how to address these issues. The following section highlights best practices to overcome many of the common barriers and challenges to successful e-prescribing.

Deploying E-Prescribing: Ten Keys to Success

1. Physicians must first determine whether the best path for the practice is stand-alone e-prescribing or a full electronic health record. Stand-alone e-prescribing is relatively inexpensive and easy to implement compared to a full electronic health record. However, a full electronic health record offers more comprehensive functionality.

2. The practice should set a clear vision and objectives for what it hopes to accomplish through e-prescribing. Examples include:

   • Move toward paperless, well-informed medication management process;

- Commit to using the technology throughout the practice to ensure that the greatest benefits can be realized;
- Improve patient safety by reducing medication errors and adverse events;
- Reduce prescription costs by prescribing on formulary and selecting lower-cost alternatives such as generics;
- Save prescriber and staff time by reducing unnecessary calls and faxes related to medication management;
- Improve patient convenience;
- Improve patient adherence with needed medications; and,
- Maximize bonus potential under the Medicare e-prescribing incentive program.

3. Prescribers should implement and use all e-prescribing services to realize maximum benefit and position their practices to qualify for federal incentives tied to meaningful use of electronic health records. This includes generating a medication list (with information from PBMs or pharmacies); selecting medications; transmitting prescriptions electronically using the applicable standards; warning the prescriber of possible undesirable or unsafe situations; providing information on lower-cost, therapeutically appropriate alternatives; and providing information on formulary or tiered formulary medications, patient eligibility, and authorization requirements received electronically from the patient's drug plan. To be eligible for e-prescribing bonus payments under Medicare, physicians must comply with these requirements.[11]

4. Physicians and their staff should thoughtfully consider workflow changes in order to optimize e-prescribing. For example, medication management process and workflows may change once the practice implements e-prescribing. Roles and responsibilities related to medication management may change with automation. Prior to e-prescribing, a physician office may not even ask patients about drug coverage or what pharmacy they use. With e-prescribing, the technology automatically checks the patient's drug coverage and the patient-specific formulary is available to the physician to inform the prescribing process. With e-prescribing, the front desk staff should double-check the patient's drug coverage and confirm his or her choice of pharmacy. Another example of workflow change relates to the management of

prescription renewals. With e-prescribing, the practice may agree that a nurse or medical assistant can handle prescription renewals for certain routine medications and needs physician approval for others. Without e-prescribing, it would be difficult to implement this type of change as easily. This modification of workflow that is enabled by e-prescribing can streamline the process to authorize prescription renewals and improve patient care and service. It is critical to commit time during implementation for training and workflow integration in order to get the best results.

5. It is important to integrate patient demographic information from the practice management system with the e-prescribing software before implementing the system. Without this information, prescribers have to enter patient data one at a time. Typically vendors offer an interface that can save a great deal of time. Note, however, that they may charge for this service. If, for some reason, the practice cannot automate the process, a staff member should preload the information into the system either all at once or before the next day's appointments. Integrating the data will increase efficiency and make it easier to start using e-prescribing.

6. Designate an e-prescribing expert in the practice who can take responsibility for the transition to e-prescribing. The expert or champion could be a physician, technician, or other staff member. This person becomes very proficient and is the go-to person for all aspects of e-prescribing. This staff member can play a lead role in addressing technical and workflow-related questions and should serve as the liaison with the technology vendor, practice staff, and pharmacies. He or she also helps ensure that the system is fully functional and that all prescribers and staff are appropriately trained.

7. Complete and effective training is the best way to integrate e-prescribing into a physician practice. Physicians and staff will not be able to learn all the features of the system in one session, so it will be necessary to schedule multiple sessions over a few months. Request self-guided training materials such as webinars, online tutorials, or implementation guides from the technology vendor, and be sure to ask about any costs associated with timing, training, and the method of training.

8. Communicate with patients about e-prescribing and explain what it means. Patients typically respond positively to e-prescribing, associating it with state-of-the-art care that is safe, accurate, and more convenient. Sending prescriptions allows patients to make fewer trips to the pharmacy. Patients should allow an hour or two before going to the pharmacy to pick up their prescription. Signage, phone line messages, and patient reminder cards help patients remember to come to the office prepared with their preferred pharmacy information and to encourage them to call their pharmacy rather than the physician office with requests for prescription renewals.

9. Avoid queuing or "batching" new prescriptions before sending them to pharmacies electronically. Send prescriptions to pharmacies immediately to ensure that the pharmacy has adequate time to process the prescription before the patient arrives. Batching prescriptions and releasing them all at certain times during the day may result in unnecessary calls from pharmacies, further delaying the patient's receipt of the medication.

10. Finally, it is critical to seek out customer support from the technology vendor for pharmacy and medication management related issues. A vendor will likely be able to fix the problem, or if it is related to the network, will alert Surescripts. Everyone in the practice should be familiar with how to report support issues to the technology vendor and should understand that they must do so timely and with the needed details.

Evolution of E-Prescribing and Beyond

E-prescribing will reach mainstream adoption with over 75 percent penetration within the next five years, leading to safer, more cost-effective, and efficient prescribing with better patient outcomes. The capabilities of the technology will continue to evolve, including the addition of prescription change and prescription cancel messages, real-time benefit checking, electronic prior authorization, structured SIG (instructions), and the improved use of prescription history to better inform the prescribing process and medication management.

There will also be opportunities to leverage the national infrastructure that has been built to enable electronic prescribing and bring additional value to the nation's healthcare system. For example, the prescription history information that is made available by the nation's pharmacies and PBMs can be used to improve decision making and the safety and quality of care beyond the ambulatory setting. With the trend toward consumer engagement and increasing adoption of personal health records, e-prescribing and prescription history information can serve as valuable vehicles to populate personal health records with individuals' medication lists.

The e-prescribing infrastructure may also be leveraged to enable broader clinical information exchange. Clinical summaries can be standardized and sent electronically among providers and between providers and patients to document transitions in care and streamline communications. The e-prescribing technology and the medication and other clinical information that flows among payers, physicians, pharmacies, and patients has the potential to offer innovative solutions to improve medication compliance and adherence as well as contribute to better care coordination, more effective cost management, and improved health outcomes.

This is an exciting time in healthcare. With new treatments and technologies on the market, we can transform our system, and e-prescribing is on the forefront of that change.

—⚉—

Kate Berry is the Senior Vice President of Market Development for Sure-Scripts, which is the country's largest electronic prescribing network. The Surescripts network is used every day by thousands of prescribers across all 50 states to electronically access prescription information and route prescriptions. Ms. Berry is also the Executive Director of the Center for Improving Medication Management, which helps physicians and patients optimally use technology to improve medication approval, prescription, and use.

—∭—

[1] National Association of Chain Drug Stores,"Industry Facts-at-a-Glance," http://www.nacds.org/wmspage.cfm?parm1=6536 (accessed January 25, 2010).

[2] Institute of Medicine, "Preventing Medication Errors: Quality Chasm Series," http://www.iom.edu/Reports/2006/Preventing-Medication-Errors-Quality-Chasm-Series.aspx (accessed January 25, 2010).

[3] Health Information Technology: For the Future of Health and Care, http://healthit.hhs.gov/portal/server.pt?open=512&mode=2&cached=true&objID=1220, (accessed January 25, 2010).

[4] Center for Information Technology Leadership, "The Value of Computerized Provider Order Entry in Ambulatory Settings," www.citl.org/research/ACPOE_Executive_Preview.pdf (accessed January 25, 2010).

[5] Gorman Health Group, "Options to Increase E-Prescribing in Medicare: Reducing Medication Errors and Generation up to $29 Billion in Savings for the Federal Government," http://www.pcmanet.org/assets/2008-03-25_Research_GHG-PCMA%20Options%20to%20Increase%20E-prescribing%20in%20Medicare%20July%2007%20FINAL.pdf (accessed January 25, 2010).

[6] Agency for Healthcare Quality and Research, "Doctor's use of e-prescribing systems linked to formulary data can boost drug cost savings," http://www.ahrq.gov/research/jan09/0109RA1.htm (accessed January 25, 2010).

[7] Paula P. Cook, M.D., et al., "Reduction in Antimicrobial Use Following Implementation of a Electronic Medical Record Associated with a Decrease in Rate of Clostridium difficile Infection at a Tertiary-Care Hospital," *Journal of Antimicrobial Chemotherapy* 53, (2004) 853-859.

[8] 2005 IMS Health: National Sales Perspective (2004 Data Analysis) & IMS Health NPA.

[9] Electronic Prescribing Readiness Assessment, http://www.getrxconnected.org (accessed January 25, 2010).

[10] The Center for Improving Medication Management, http://thecimm.org/ (accessed January 25, 2010).

[11] The Centers for Medicare & Medicaid Services, "Overview: Electronic Prescribing (eRx) Incentive Program," http://www.cms.hhs.gov/ERXincentive/ (accessed January 25, 2010).

CHAPTER 11

It's Time for Telemedicine:
Greater Access, Better Quality, and Lower Costs

Jac J. Davies and Nancy L. Vorhees

—ɷ—

Editor's Introduction

Videoconferencing is a staple of the business world. It can connect individuals from all parts of the globe in real time to exchange ideas and solve problems. While the typical videoconference doesn't involve discussions of life and death, it can if it is between you and your doctor. This kind of technology, while widespread in nearly every other aspect of our lives, is relatively rare in healthcare. It is not because it is new. Telemedicine was an early development by NASA in the 1960s. It is not because of a lack of value. As leaders like Inland Northwest Health Services have proven, telemedicine greatly expands access to specialty care, enhances health education and allows for remote patient monitoring, clinician training, electronic data exchange, and more. Unfortunately, structural barriers of today's healthcare system, like payment models and burdensome regulation, have hampered its growth and prevented more patients from utilizing its benefits. Telemedicine possesses a rich past and productive present, and if the existing barriers can be broken down, it has a very bright future.

—ɷ—

The healthcare system faces provider shortages, patients with complex health conditions, and decreasing reimbursements. But just as exercise offers a single treatment for multiple health conditions, telemedicine offers a single solution to multiple system ills. For providers, it allows distant organizations to share healthcare resources and expand services. For patients, telemedicine increases access to specialists, saves money by reducing travel costs, and most importantly, improves the quality of care.

What Is Telemedicine?

According to the American Telemedicine Association, "Telemedicine is the use of medical information exchanged from one site to another via electronic communications to improve patients' health status."[1] A broader term, "telehealth," is often used to include not only clinical care but also health education, professional training, and administrative support functions—all conducted with participants at different locations. Telemedicine programs use a wide variety of technology including videoconferencing, remote monitoring of diagnostic devices, and electronic access to health data. There are approximately 200 such networks operating in the United States, linking more than 2,500 institutions nationwide.

The technology first emerged in the 1960s when NASA developed remote medical monitoring systems for astronauts in space flight. To test the new technologies, NASA initiated a number of pilot programs delivering healthcare services to patients in remote locations such as the Papago Indian Reservation in Arizona. Over the next decade, other pilot projects established two-way audiovisual connections to allow delivery of care between distant locations in Nebraska, Alaska, and Massachusetts. These early systems used closed-circuit television, microwave circuits, and satellites to make the connections. While satellites are still used today, the transfer of information is more likely to occur via standard telephone lines, ISDN, dedicated T-1 lines, high-speed fiber optics, or the Internet.

Northwest TeleHealth

Northwest TeleHealth, a program of Inland Northwest Health Services in Spokane, Washington, was established in 1997 to help deliver healthcare services in rural communities. Washington has geographic, cultural, economic, and technological divides that separate urban areas from its exceptionally rural regions. The high desert, mountainous terrain, and harsh winters of eastern Washington make travel between communities difficult, expensive, and, sometimes, even dangerous.

From its early beginnings connecting a handful of sites, Northwest TeleHealth has grown to a mature telemedicine network linking 65 locations with more than 100 videoconference devices. Northwest TeleHealth network member locations are independent healthcare facilities that include regional medical centers, rural hospitals and clinics, mental health facilities, corrections facilities, and Indian health centers. By transmitting live video, voice, and data, Northwest TeleHealth makes it possible for patients, physicians, administrators, and healthcare educators to interact and share information. These linkages occur not only within the Northwest TeleHealth network but also among telemedicine networks around the country. In 2008, Northwest TeleHealth hosted more than 2,000 videoconference events, with connections ranging from Minneapolis to Guam to the Aleutian Islands in Alaska.

Like many other telemedicine programs, Northwest TeleHealth services fall into three general categories: 1) clinical care; 2) distance education; and 3) administrative and operational planning and coordination.

Clinical Care
Healthcare providers and patients use the Northwest TeleHealth network for the most traditional application of telemedicine: remote patient consults. Patients who live in rural communities are able to obtain access to specialists via their local critical access hospital rather than driving long distances for a short visit in Spokane. For example, neurologists have used the system to monitor progress of individuals recovering from strokes or with Parkinson's disease, and diabetes educators provide personal counseling to newly diagnosed patients. Northwest TeleHealth has helped a patient in rural Montana receive care from a geneticist in Salt Lake City, Utah, without having to travel. A patient in Post Falls, Idaho, received a remote clinical consultation from a specialist at the University of British Columbia Hospital in Vancouver, BC. Another patient in Colville, Washington, received services via Northwest TeleHealth from a physician located on Texas, almost 2,000 miles away.

In general, the care protocols used for remote consults are the same as those used for in-person consults. Procedures that require physical contact with the patient, such as checking blood pressure, can be accommodated by a medical assistant or other healthcare aide in the exam room with the patient.

While all benefits have yet to be realized, the biggest advantage of the technology is the education the hospital provides to the community via telehealth, according to Vicky Johnson, Site Coordinator of East Adams Rural Hospital: "We think the value is there in the community education and patient results."

Patient Barbara Tillson agrees. At first, she was "a little skeptical just thinking about a computer and how cold it could be." Her skepticism vanished immediately. "This was not cold at all," she said. "I really enjoyed it. [The educator] was so nice and so down to earth and I really learned a lot from her. I could ask questions. It was great. It was a really good experience."

Beyond individual patient consults, healthcare facilities are using the system to share resources and improve the delivery of care. Small rural hospitals with emergency rooms that are frequently staffed with mid-level professionals take advantage of a TeleER program operated by Northwest TeleHealth to gain immediate access to emergency department specialists in Spokane. This system allows specialists to view and interact with patients and their families as well as rural healthcare providers while allowing the specialists to review test results and diagnostic images. The augmented information sharing allows the on-site provider and the remote specialist to collaboratively develop a treatment plan, resulting in better patient outcomes.

A nine-year-old boy in rural Newport, Washington, suffered a freak bicycle accident that resulted in a handlebar being driven through his heart. He was taken to the emergency room at Newport Community Hospital, a 24-bed critical access facility where the ER director is Physician Assistant Chris McGlothlen. Images and lab results were transmitted electronically to Deaconess Medical Center, a 388-bed Level 2 trauma facility 50 miles away in Spokane. TeleER was used to facilitate communication between the two facilities and with Northwest MedStar, the region's critical air ambulance service. Because of the available technology, all providers on the care team were able to rapidly organize treatment and transport, and the boy survived a potentially life-threatening injury.

Chris McGlothlen noted, "TeleER makes care flow smoother and gets the patient where they need to be sooner—resulting in better outcomes. As a small community hospital, we have limited on-site resources. TeleER give us immediate access to urban specialists and patient data. Having this expertise at our fingertips allows us to increase the level of care to the residents of this rural community."

Distance Education
Healthcare providers in rural communities have limited access to professional education. Obtaining necessary education and training usually means long travel to urban academic medical centers, an option that is expensive and often not feasible for small facilities with limited staff. Alternatively, rural healthcare providers can use web-based training, but such tools do not allow for the interaction and instructor support that is inherent in classroom-based learning.

Northwest TeleHealth has extensive experience delivering distance professional health education via videoconferencing. This system allows two-way, real-time interaction between instructors and students and a more engaging environment for adult learners. Videoconference-based distance education also enables interaction between students at remote locations, reducing the feeling of isolation of many healthcare providers practicing alone in rural communities.

Among Northwest TeleHealth's educational offerings is EMS Live@Nite, a program targeted at rural emergency medical services personnel. This monthly program reaches more than 300 EMS providers across Washington, Oregon, Idaho, Montana, and Alaska including very remote villages in the Aleutian Islands. 85 percent of the participants are volunteers who hold full-time jobs during the day. The program is invaluable to many individuals, as travel out of their service areas for state-required continuing education is often difficult as well as costly.

Northwest TeleHealth also provides access to professional education offerings from around the country, such as "Acute Stroke Assessment and Treatment," "Moderate (Conscious) Sedation," psychiatry grand rounds, and brain tumor boards. This easy access is beneficial not only to rural healthcare practitioners but also to anyone who has limited time and cannot drive across town to participate in needed training.

Administrative and Operational Planning and Coordination
Using telehealth systems for administrative and operational planning and coordination within and among healthcare organizations is
another way to reduce healthcare costs and improve the overall effectiveness of the system. Administrators and staff of separate healthcare
facilities under a single corporate umbrella utilize Northwest Tele-
Health for meetings without incurring travel costs. State agencies use
the system to communicate potential regulatory changes or solicit
input on program activities across multiple health care organizations. For example, the Washington State Department of Health held
multiple statewide rulemaking workshops via telehealth to take comments on proposed rule changes related to the state's cancer registry.
"It is an hour just for us to go to Spokane, Washington, so it is two
hours of travel for a one-hour meeting. Travel time and costs restrict
which meetings we could attend," said Vicky Johnson.

Northwest TeleHealth has also played a key role in regional
emergency preparedness. All rural counties and medical centers
are required to have hazard plans as part of the National Incident
Management System, creating a unified incident response structure for federal, state, and local branches of government. Hospitals
across the region use Northwest TeleHealth to conduct emergency
preparedness planning meetings and training sessions with the
emergency management and emergency medical service agencies
related to bioterrorism and pandemic response, mass casualty
management, and emergency communications. The system has
also been used during disaster response exercises, providing an
alternate mode of communication among agencies.

Because of the many public and private sector agencies at the
federal, state, and local levels involved in emergency response,
communication during an emergency can be complex. One of the
hospitals in Spokane has been identified as the Regional Control
Hospital (RCH). When emergency management declares a local,
state, regional, or national disaster, the RCH is the first line of
communication for all facilities that need to respond to a medical emergency. The RCH in turn communicates with the local
Combined Communication Center, which in turn communicates
with state and federal agencies. Northwest TeleHealth provides a
critical communication link within this network.

Barriers to Utilization of Telemedicine

While the use of telemedicine has grown significantly in the past decade, it is by no means widespread across the U.S. healthcare system. Why has adoption taken so long when the benefits of the technology are so clear? The reasons are explored below.

Reimbursement
In telemedicine's infancy, reimbursement for healthcare services delivered at a distance was a major obstacle to its use. Insurers were not convinced that remote delivery of care was as effective as in-person healthcare visits. As the technology matured and research demonstrated the efficacy of telemedicine, both public insurers such as Medicare and Medicaid and private insurers such as CIGNA and Aetna have been gradually adding telemedicine to their list of covered services. However, many services that could be delivered by telemedicine are still not reimbursed by insurers, and there is wide variation among insurance companies in their willingness to pay. The patchwork of reimbursement policies makes it difficult for telemedicine networks to be certain that their technological investment will pay off.

According to the American Telemedicine Association, many telemedicine programs have successfully applied the following approaches to obtaining reimbursement from private payers for telemedicine services:

- Treating telemedicine services as usual and customary medical practices. Actions to try to identify telemedicine consultations as different or requiring "special" coding generally proved counter-productive and of limited value.
- Sending letters to their private payers, to include:
  - The intent to provide such services, using telemedicine as the normal course of business;
  - Notification of future claim submittals; and,
  - Encouraging questions and comments from the private payer.

While Medicare has begun reimbursing for some telemedicine services, so far it has limited that coverage to patients residing in

Medical Shortage Areas or rural health professional shortage areas. There is little logic to this limitation as health professional shortage areas focus on primary care and often the best use of telemedicine is improving access to specialists. Because of state flexibility, there has been a more widespread adoption of reimbursement for telemedicine services in state Medicaid programs. Thirty-five states now have authorized reimbursement for some telemedicine services to increase access to specialists and reduce transportation costs.

One promising trend for telemedicine networks is contract-based service agreements between facilities. For example, a tertiary care hospital may establish a contract with a correctional facility to deliver healthcare services to offenders and triage any cases that may need to be transported. The correctional facility saves on transport and staffing costs, and the hospital has a reliable revenue source that is not subject to the vagaries of health insurance claims.

"It is less expensive to house offenders in a lower-custody environment than in a higher-custody environment," said Marty Lyons, healthcare manager at Coyote Ridge Corrections Center (CRCC), a minimum-custody facility on forty acres in the city of Connell. CRCC is surrounded by farmland in Washington State's Franklin County; the nearest medical specialist or mental healthcare provider is at least 45 minutes away. Lyons added that by eliminating the "added cost of staff time for transport, arrangements at another facility to fit into their mental health scheduling, cost of fuel and wear and tear on vehicles, telemedicine has represented great cost savings. We can give offenders the tools to help work through their mental health issues and they are able to have a fallback plan by having access. It has been very beneficial."

Licensure, Certification, and Credentialing
Telemedicine programs by their nature have the ability to deliver care across state lines. When the goal is reducing costs, sharing resources across widely distributed healthcare organizations makes sense. However, healthcare provider licensure is still very much state-specific. To practice in multiple states, providers must obtain licenses and meet widely varying continuing education requirements in each state. This is time-consuming and costly, and discourages many telemedicine programs from extending their geographic reach.

The Federation of State Medical Boards of the United States has been working to address the interstate licensure issue. A special committee of the Federation has been advising state medical boards that have begun drafting regulation regarding interstate practice. Through this work, the committee has developed a model act that is available to state medical boards to use when drafting regulations related to telemedicine licensure.

Beyond individual licensure issues, certification and approval of different types of telemedicine programs is also a state issue. State professional boards such as pharmacy and physical therapy may need to certify that new telemedicine-based programs meet board-imposed requirements. Again, this means that telemedicine programs must invest resources in understanding individual state requirements and convince the state boards that their program will work.

A new barrier that has emerged is facility-specific credentialing and privileging. Until recently the Joint Commission on the Accreditation of Healthcare Organizations (JCAHO) permitted accredited facilities to "credential by proxy," where rural hospitals could accept credentialing of urban or receiving facilities. However, CMS is now forcing JCAHO to require individual credentialing and privileging of each provider in each rural facility. This rapidly becomes unwieldy for providers and telemedicine programs. The telemedicine community is working with members of Congress to develop laws that would allow acceptance of reciprocal privileging.

Lack of Institutional Support

Telemedicine programs need extensive institutional support, both from a technological and leadership perspective. Although the costs of telemedicine devices have decreased significantly in the last decade, implementing a telemedicine program is still an expensive proposition. Whether an organization is planning to operate its own program or simply intends to contract for services from a regional telemedicine network, the organization's leadership must recognize the value of the service and be willing to invest. That investment includes assuring that there is sufficient network connectivity to support high-speed, high-quality videoconferencing, and available technical staff for supporting the system.

Because any new technology can be challenging to staff, an organization's leaders also have to make it clear they expect telemedicine systems to be used. This institutional support can help individuals to get past any initial hesitation about using the equipment and assure long-term success. To develop that support, relationship-building is critical. Someone at the executive level needs to own the program, and someone at the operational level needs to have responsibility for growing and directing the program. The telemedicine program needs to align with the mission and goals of the organization, and must develop a business case that demonstrates positive return on investment.

Lack of Provider Support
One potential advantage of telemedicine is the ability for patients to get access to specialists who might not otherwise be available in their community. However, to realize this benefit, specialists have to be willing to use the technology. The reality is that many specialists in this country, especially high-demand specialties such as pediatric psychiatry, have more patients than they can handle. They have no incentive for adding additional workload by seeing patients via telemedicine systems.

Addressing the licensure and reimbursement issues described above would help mitigate this problem. Specialists anywhere in the country could provide services, tapping into telemedicine networks to fill in any gaps in their schedules. Further, telemedicine programs need to make the technology as easy as possible so that seeing a patient via telehealth is as easy as having a patient walk into the exam room. This includes not only videoconference equipment, but also scheduling and coordination between the provider's office and the patient's location.

Evolution of Telemedicine Networks
Telemedicine networks have evolved at a very local level. Decisions are made based on local needs and operations are conducted based on local demands. While standards for electronic health information exchange are emerging nationally, standards for communication between telemedicine networks are less robust. Connections among networks can be cumbersome and resource-intensive. Trained telehealth staff need to stand by to

fix any problems that might occur. Doctors, staff, and patients have all grown accustomed to picking up a telephone and having a trouble-free connection to anywhere in the world. Telemedicine will not achieve widespread adoption until its systems are just as easy to use.

Separation of Telemedicine and Health Information Technology
In many healthcare organizations, telemedicine programs evolved separately and are supported separately from the institution's health information technology group. This is also true for the healthcare industry as a whole, resulting in diverging technology planning, competition for resources, and duplication of effort. While there has been some progress at the national level in aligning health information technology and telehealth initiatives, the divergent path of the two focus areas is still readily apparent.

Now more than ever, it is critical that telemedicine and health information technology programs align their efforts. There is a synergistic relationship between telemedicine and e-health. To be effective, the remote delivery of care relies on the ready availability of a patient's health information. In addition, any care that is delivered remotely needs to be captured in the patient's local medical record for use by the primary care provider. Telemedicine will only be truly successful when there is a strong health information exchange infrastructure.

Emerging Opportunities

In this era of health reform, telemedicine is one technology that has real potential to significantly improve the delivery and reduce the cost of healthcare. The telemedicine industry has seen considerable growth and maturation since its early beginnings in the 1960s, but widespread utilization has been much slower than many industry analysts predicted.

Because of the current pressures on the healthcare system, there are tremendous opportunities for telemedicine to finally become a key component of healthcare delivery. The demands for better, smarter utilization of existing healthcare resources are growing. Lawmakers, employers, and healthcare providers are beginning to recognize that telemedicine is a viable option to address this need. Telemedicine programs and healthcare organizations must respond by leveraging health information exchange efforts, simplifying the technology, working to reduce policy barriers, and collaborating across programs to promote connectivity. With these actions, telemedicine will emerge as a critical part of the U.S. healthcare system in the new decade.

—m—

Jac J. Davies is the Director of Northwest TeleHealth, Regional Outreach, and health@work for Inland Northwest Health Services. Ms. Davies is responsible for managing a large regional telemedicine network, providing continuing education and support for rural healthcare providers, and promoting employee wellness.

Nancy L. Vorhees is the Chief Operating Officer for Inland Northwest Health Services, a non-profit organization providing shared services to hospitals and physician offices. Ms. Vorhees is responsible for a large regional telehealth system, a community health education program, and the region's major air ambulance service.

—m—

[1] American Telemedicine Association, "Telemedicine Defined," http://www.americantelemed.org/i4a/pages/index.cfm?pageID=3333 (accessed January 25, 2010).

CHAPTER 12

Finally: A Look into One of the Nation's First Statewide Health Information Exchanges

Harris A. Frankel, M.D. and Deborah Bass

—⟩⟩⟨⟨—

Editor's Introduction

Former Speaker of the House Tip O'Neill famously said that "all politics is local." The same can be said for healthcare. Patients seek care from doctors and nurses they know and trust. Hospitals are often at the center of their respective communities. So it is only appropriate that efforts to connect and modernize our healthcare system through health information technology start at the local level. From employer and physician leadership to competing hospitals turned collaborators to cheerleading from the state's highest officials, leaders in Nebraska have demonstrated the success that is possible through partnership, commitment, and determination. This chapter explores what they have accomplished so far, how they have succeeded, and what they will do in the future.

—⟩⟩⟨⟨—

Hurricane Katrina and its devastating aftermath taught us many valuable lessons. One of the most important was to sharpen the focus on the critical need to modernize the American health system through health information technology. While the vast majority of patients and providers saw paper medical records literally washed away, places like the Veterans Administration and the National Cancer Institute showed that accessing electronic medical information in an emergency saves lives and saves money. Leaders in Nebraska have taken that lesson to heart and built one of the most robust health information exchanges in the country. The Nebraska Health Information Initiative (NeHII) is a statewide, non-proprietary, interoperable, secure exchange for health information, connecting physicians, hospitals, pharmacies, labs, imaging centers, and payers together. It is this kind of cutting-edge, patient-protected technology enabled by dedicated, statewide leadership and collaboration that is improving the health and lives of Nebraskans.

NeHII, one of the first statewide health information exchanges (HIE) in the nation, serves more than 1.2 million individuals across Nebraska. It was the first HIE to launch with a complete operational set of features and functions, providing physicians with clinical messaging through an online virtual health record. This longitudinal view, incorporating data from multiple sources, includes the patient's medical lab and X-ray results, transcription reports, medication history, allergy notification, insurance eligibility, and demographic data and referrals that are all delivered at the point of care at a speed which physicians can live with. Current statistics show that NeHII has completed more than 96 percent of requested matches in less than two seconds.

Although the virtual health record can be accessed through any browser, NeHII encourages participation by providing easy-to-use CCHIT-certified EHR and e-prescribing solutions to physicians who do not already have the applications. The ASP technology frees physicians from the expense of hardware acquisition and IT support for a license fee of $52 per month (less than the price of cable television). Approximately two dozen practitioners have taken advantage of the EHR and e-prescribing solutions thus far, with approximately 500 physician members of UniNet, a not-for-profit physician hospital organization, slated to begin using the application as their e-prescribing solution in early 2010.

The Beginning

Building such a robust technology to cover all 77,000+ square miles of Nebraska did not come easy, nor did it happen overnight. The seeds of NeHII date back to 2005, when the Nebraska Biomedical Informatics Project identified an economic opportunity to implement a business and technology infrastructure to deliver high-quality, cost-effective care to all citizens of Nebraska. This original initiative included representatives from the University of Nebraska, University of Nebraska Medical Center, Creighton University, Alegent Health, and Greater Omaha Chamber of Commerce, as well as then governor and now United States Senator Mike Johanns and then lieutenant governor (now current Nebraska governor) Dave Heineman. Soon other key leaders joined, including the Nebraska Hospital Association, the Nebraska Medical Association, representatives from state government, and Blue Cross Blue Shield of Nebraska.

The group considered relying on the development of a statewide electronic medical record using a central data repository, but instead a plan to adopt a hybrid federated model began to emerge. A federated architecture, one in which the data remains at the provider site, prevents co-mingling of data and avoids the use of a central data repository. A hybrid federated model allows the data to remain separate, but each provider's data interoperates with the HIE through an "edge" server that resides in the same facility as the HIE. When an HIE user requests information, the system uses a Master Patient Index and Record Locator Service to match the request to the right patient.

The group developed an initial business plan and released a request for information seeking data on software architectures to support the requirements of the HIE.

Although similar efforts in other states and communities were struggling to obtain start-up funding, NeHII leaders were able to successfully underwrite their planning efforts. Funding was provided by Blue Cross Blue Shield of Nebraska, which donated more than $1 million in support of the collaborative, and virtually all the stakeholder participants dedicated substantial personnel resources to the effort.

However, the excitement and promise of the initiative were soon eclipsed by the tough issues involved in formulating business plans, policies, funding models, and a technology strategy. In March 2007, after progress had stalled in the midst of struggles around the commitment of adequate resources to focus on the initiative, Alegent Health, a major health system in Omaha and Nebraska's second largest employer, sponsored a two-day Decision Acceleration session on behalf of NeHII.[1] This intense strategic planning process produced a clear vision, mission, goals, and objectives, along with a renewed commitment to moving forward.

Decision acceleration sessions such as these are designed to produce high-quality strategic plans in a short amount of time through an intense effort of collecting and synthesizing information. The activities bring together the right people at the right time in a single location to work through a set of brief, highly focused assignments.

More than 75 attendees participated, including physicians, hospital executives, employers, community members, and patients. Not only did the session produce a clear plan for the future of the exchange, but it also contributed to the development of value statements for the stakeholder groups.

During the highly interactive strategy session, an artist graphically translated the discussion, and a horizon map for NeHII emerged. This visual blueprint, created on a white wall as the participants worked through ideas, was punctuated by colorful illustrations of goals and objectives over a five-year time frame.

The NeHII horizon map was rooted by a vision and a mission statement that was a product of the discussions:

> NeHII will be the leading, trusted entity to facilitate the valued electronic exchange and accessibility of health information through a collaborative network. It will empower consumers and providers to effectively utilize resources to achieve optimal health outcomes.

Goals for the first year included: the identification of data exchange infrastructures in Nebraska, alignment with key partners, communication of value propositions, building critical mass in HIE membership, determination of the database model for the HIE, and finally the successful completion of a pilot.

Goals for the two- to three-year time frame were to expand the system to 300,000 lives, with active participation of 25 to 30 percent of key stakeholders. Objectives included evaluation of system use, agreement on a PHR (personal health record) approach, e-prescribing, medication reconciliation, and results reporting with imaging.

For the three- to five-year time frame, goals included coordination of care and expansion across the state to include all patients and providers. Objectives were to determine the next levels of functionality, achieve measureable improvement, implement the agreed upon PHR, and achieve active participation of at least 50 percent of the key stakeholders.

Continuing Efforts

Immediately after the decision acceleration session, NeHII leaders engaged Bass & Associates, an Omaha-based IT consulting, advisory, and managed services firm, to "make this happen," with instructions to move forward aggressively "asking forgiveness, not permission." The desire for an entrepreneurial approach was made clear by the selection of a group that was clearly competitive, accustomed to acting quickly, and had a history of prior successes with a number of the stakeholders.

Another reason NeHII leaders used the model was to keep overhead expenses at a minimum. They had no brick and mortar to support, and were able to contract out for the necessary skills for only the period of time required, avoiding the burden of fully employed and benefited employees whose skills may not have remained the best fit as the project progressed.

The initial Bass & Associates workforce was lean, consisting of a project manager and interim executive director. Under the direction of a highly engaged board of directors, a project charter and plan were developed. Interim executive director Deb Bass and project manager Chris Henkenius supervised the writing and release of an RFP, and the top two vendor candidates were invited to Omaha for a series of product demonstrations with area physicians and other stakeholders.

Articles of incorporation and bylaws were filed in May 2008 to establish NeHII as a 501(c)(3) nonprofit organization. A board of directors was elected, with Dr. Harris Frankel named president.[2] Having a full-time practicing neurologist as the board leader was not only important for delivering the physician perspective to the effort, but was also instrumental in establishing credibility with other physicians.

Board committees were formed to focus on important issues and to support and expand the NeHII operation. They saw firsthand the power of an electronic exchange when members and stakeholders visited with the Physicians Medical Group of Santa Cruz County, an HIE with more than 600 active users that had been in existence for thirteen years.

As the group boarded the plane for Santa Cruz, doubts remained that an HIE could be a reality in Nebraska. But throughout the two-day visit, the group witnessed the impact that HIE was having on the quality and safety of the citizens of Santa Cruz County. Physicians from small primary care practices to major health systems talked about the benefits to patients of having all their health information available at the point of care, as well as the ability to reduce redundant lab and X-ray testing, more accurately assess treatment plans, use e-prescribing to gauge medication compliance by patients, the ability to speed the referral process to specialty practices after the identification of disease processes, and educating and engaging patients in their care plans with the use of the electronic trending reports at the point of care. A tired but determined group headed back to Nebraska, invigorated by the realization that a statewide HIE was not only well worth the effort, but within their capabilities.

By July 2008, NeHII had published a website and signed a letter of intent with Axolotl for the core technology and infrastructure. In the meantime, NeHII leaders had settled on a financial model. Implementation funding was supported through Class B memberships paid by the pilot participants according to the bed size of the facility. Dollar amounts ranged from $25,000 for hospitals with 150 or fewer beds to $250,000 for those with more than 500 beds. Class B members could also elect NeHII board members at one vote per dollar contributed.

By November 2008, an agreement had been executed with Axolotl, and the first draft of security and privacy policies were in the final stages of development.

Completion of the privacy and security policies as well as the development of the technical environment in which they were implemented required long and arduous hours of in-depth testing.

A test lab was established and teams from the pilot organizations met regularly to test core functionality and features of the system to make certain the data exchanged was accurate, and that the operational processes were accurately reflected. As stakeholders were able to view the functionality in a test environment, their comprehension of the system improved and the pieces fell into place.

In January 2009, data migration began, and an operations manual was created. The pilot, using the live system, was officially launched just three months later, in March 2009.

Ken Lawonn, NeHII Board Vice President and CIO of Alegent Health, commented, "We should have moved to pilot implementation sooner. Once we brought up the pilot, much of the oppositional behavior was eliminated because the system worked so well."

The Pilot

On April 2, 2009, Gov. Dave Heineman announced the launch of the NeHII pilot to a cheering, standing-room-only crowd of physicians, business and community leaders, stakeholders, patients, and the public.

The 90-day pilot, completed in June of 2009, connected nearly a dozen major hospitals and facilities affiliated with the Nebraska Medical Center, Children's Hospital and Medical Center, Methodist Health System, Alegent Health, and Blue Cross Blue Shield of Nebraska. After the board of directors at NeHII's first annual meeting on July 9, 2009, in Kearney, Nebraska, unanimously declared the pilot a success, the project moved to statewide implementation.

Three agreed-upon factors demonstrated the success of the HIE: 1) ease of use and acceptance by physicians; 2) the delivery of e-prescribing, clinical messaging, and referrals; and 3) privacy and security of clinical health information. But the greatest surprise of the pilot was simply how well the technology worked. At a recent site visit with representatives from Arizona and South Dakota, the chief information officers from the pilot organizations agreed that NeHII was one of the easiest implementation projects they had ever experienced. There were no hiccups with the technology, and in fact, it worked amazingly well.

New Horizons

After plans for statewide implementation were announced, Mary Lanning Memorial Hospital in Hastings, Nebraska, followed by Great Plains Regional Medical Center in North Platte became the next hospital systems to join NeHII, and a significant number of additional organizations have provided letters of commitment.

Patients and the public continue to believe in the benefits of accessible health information. Opt-out rates have consistently remained low, between 1.4 percent and 2.1 percent, confirming consumers' understanding and trust in the benefits of health information exchange in Nebraska. A portion of this understanding can be attributed to consumer education provided at the point of care since the initial implementation, as well as the educational materials and training curriculum for intake personnel.

Meeting of the Minds

Many leaders of HIE implementations would agree that an estimated 15 percent of the effort is directed toward the business and technology solution, while 85 percent involves managing the political battles and achievement of stakeholder capital necessary to sustain progress.

Nowhere was this more evident than in the early days of authoring privacy and security policy. Amid fears and concerns, stakeholders worked to build a plan to guarantee compliance with HIPAA privacy and security regulations, while still charged with providing a system that could robustly provide adequate data to healthcare providers, when and where needed. The group struggled with audit requirements and other precautions built into electronic systems that mandated a higher level of privacy protection than that to which the paper world was accustomed.

The question of "break the glass" functionality also existed, which refers to situations when emergency room physicians, in order to obtain critical medical information, might need to over-ride the decision of an unconscious patient who had previously opted out of the HIE. The privacy experts felt it would be better to defend a violation of privacy versus risking injury or death of a patient because of a lack of access to information, although it was decided to limit this functionality until a comfort level was established on behalf of the providers and patients.

Stakeholders guarded their established processes religiously. The privacy and security professionals, along with the technical experts, and those interested in the operational aspects of the HIE, needed to know that the others complied with their require-ments, and at times, the goals of the different groups conflicted.

When angst within the ranks began to bog down the progress, leadership emerged. Determined pilot participants stepped for-ward and took accountability for tasks and completion dates, while NeHII leaders supported a solid, agreed-upon project plan that was being closely monitored by a skilled project manager with a strict project control process. To avoid continual rehashing of previous conclusions, the group maintained decision tree documents illus-trating the history and reasoning around specific decisions.

As always, relationship building was continually top of mind for the NeHII leadership, and along with a variety of other duties, it was a very important part of the scope of responsibilities for Bass & Associates. Fortunately, the NeHII stakeholders and project team fostered open communications, always looking back to the original horizon plan that had resulted from the 2007 strategy session.

HIE and the Business Community

A critical constituency was the business community. More than almost anyone else, employers have experienced firsthand the burden that rising healthcare costs places on businesses and their employ-ees. NeHII leaders met with a number of CEOs of major employers in the Omaha area to educate, engage, and ask for support.

They questioned why healthcare lagged so far behind the busi-ness world in terms of interoperability and data exchange, and wondered how this could happen in a world where business and financial systems have been sharing information globally for years. That kind of response—and the desire to fix it—were keys to gaining support from local business leaders.

Several CEOs demonstrated a willingness to help the effort in any way they could. Their support was critical, and by September 2008, NeHII was planning the pilot project with key stakeholders in Omaha.

At about the same time, a second site visit to the Rochester, New York, RHIO took place. NeHII leaders, along with a group of CEOs from the soon-to-be pilot participants, and the director of Nebraska Medicaid, Vivianne Chaumont, were introduced to state government participation. In particular, there was a new awareness of how HIE could, through improvements and efficiencies in claims processing, deliver value to Medicaid while improving services and saving taxpayer dollars.

Also observed in Rochester was the importance of the opt-out vs. opt-in approach as it relates to consumer participation in the HIE. With an opt-in method, patients must provide consent prior to their personal health information being available in the HIE. Rochester RHIO is an opt-in platform, as required by New York state law. Nebraska state law requires that an opt-in platform must be reconfirmed with participating individuals every 180 days. Realizing that this would create an administrative burden, NeHII made a decision to use the opt-out platform, providing the individual's information to the exchange unless they take action to opt themselves out of the system.

Conclusion

Today, NeHII continues to improve and expand HIE services across the state of Nebraska, with a goal to enlist 96 percent of healthcare facilities and providers within the next four years. Also being considered are further specialties and care settings, such as dentists, school nurses, extended care facilities and nursing homes, and chiropractors.

In September 2009, Nebraska Gov. Dave Heineman officially declared NeHII the State Designated Entity for the State HIE Cooperative

Agreement Program established by the Office of the National Coordinator for Health Information Technology.[3] NeHII will work in conjunction with the state of Nebraska to manage HIE grants provided by stimulus funding from the *American Recovery and Reinvestment Act*. Part of that law will provide physicians with bonus payments for the "meaningful use" of certified health information technology.

As meaningful use requirements are refined by the Office of the National Coordinator, NeHII looks to the five domains defined by the HIT Policy Committee: 1) improvement of the quality of patient care through increased patient safety, efficiency, and reduction of health disparities; 2) engaging patients and families in their healthcare; 3) improvement of care coordination; 4) improving population and public health; and 5) ensuring adequate privacy and security protections for personal health.[4]

Remarkably, the NeHII horizon map created in 2007 strongly presaged these criteria prior to their establishment by the HIT Policy Committee. The vision of the NeHII leaders, along with the synthesis of information provided by engaged healthcare professionals, patients, and business and community leaders, provided a reliable road map that has been followed since its creation, with only minor deviations.

This harmony between those who established NeHII and officials establishing meaningful use policy can certainly be considered a correlation to NeHII's success. Having essentially followed a "meaningful use" road map since 2007, NeHII has experienced a challenging journey and has executed a flawless landing into today's environment.

NeHII is now in the early stages of a statewide consumer and physician awareness campaign with an expanded and updated consumer education brochure, as well as public service radio spots, media interviews, town hall meetings, and plans for presentations before community organizations.

The exchange is also working to establish relationships with neighboring states to share data for patients who seek medical care across state lines and jurisdictions. Discussions have been held with the states of Colorado, South Dakota, Wyoming, Iowa,

Kansas, Missouri, and Minnesota regarding regional HIE connectivity scenarios that could be implemented either as extensions of NeHII, or with their statewide HIE when it becomes operational.

NeHII's road map for the future includes engaging with Nebraska public health efforts in the areas of disease surveillance, immunization registries, and public health alerts, and working to enhance the efficiencies of Medicaid operations. Also on the horizon is the development of quality analytics reporting, claims transaction processing, and consumer access to NeHII through the use of a personal health record.

While the road map gains definition and the NeHII vision grows, we remain focused on the original game plan: connecting every community across Nebraska to deliver better-quality and more cost-effective care. We believe that our success has and will serve the state of Nebraska well and will stand as a symbol of inspiration for developing HIEs across the nation.

—⚋—

Harris A. Frankel, M.D. is the President of the Nebraska Health Information Initiative, whose goal is to provide Nebraska a system for the secure exchange and use of health information. Dr. Frankel also maintains a private neurology practice in Omaha, Nebraska, and leads the Medicare Committee for the Nebraska Medical Association. Dr. Frankel is also the president of the Metro Omaha Medical Society.

Deborah Bass is the President and Chief Executive Officer of Bass & Associates, Inc., which she helped found in response to the demand for business and information technology consulting services. Bass & Associates currently employs more than 85 IT consultants offering IT services in an eleven-state region. Ms. Bass has received numerous awards, including national recognition as the Goodwill BAC Member of the Year in 2000. She also serves as the Interim Executive Director of NeHII.

—⁓—

[1] Alegent Health, "School of Radiologic Technology," http://www.alegent.com/body.cfm?id=5375 (accessed January 25, 2010).

[2] Nebraska Health Information Exchange, "NeHII Board of Directors," http://www.nehii.org/index.php?option=com_content&view=article&id=3:board-members&catid=4:other&Itemid=42 (accessed January 25, 2010).

[3] Nebraska Information Technology Commission, "eHealth News from the NITC Health Council," http://www.nitc.state.ne.us/eHc/clearing/news/2009/2009NoveHealthnewsletter.pdf (accessed January 25, 2010).

[4] Health Information Technology: For the Future of Health and Care, http://healthit.hhs.gov/portal/server.pt?open=18&objID=888532&parentname=CommunityPage&parentid=5&mode=2&in_hi_userid=11113&cached=true (accessed January 25, 2010).

About the Editor

David Merritt is Vice President and National Policy Director at the Center for Health Transformation and the Gingrich Group. The Center, headed by former Speaker Newt Gingrich, is a collaboration of leaders dedicated to transforming health and healthcare in America. Mr. Merritt advises Speaker Gingrich and leads the Center's work on national health reform and health information technology.

Mr. Merritt's writing has been widely published, including in the *Chicago Tribune*, *Boston Globe*, *Chicago Sun-Times*, *Atlanta Journal-Constitution*, and *Miami Herald*. In addition to TV and radio appearances, such as the Fox Business Channel and Bill Bennett's *Morning in America*, he is widely quoted in national and trade press, including the *Wall Street Journal* and the *Washington Post*, and is a frequent speaker in the industry. He has been a guest lecturer at the Yale School of Management and at Princeton University, at the invitation of visiting professor and former Senate Majority Leader Bill Frist. He is the editor of *Paper Kills*, winner of the 2007 book of the year award by the Health Information Management Systems Society (HIMSS).

Mr. Merritt was a health policy adviser to the presidential campaign of Senator John McCain, having served the same role with former senator Fred Thompson. He served on Virginia governor Tim Kaine's Health Information Technology Council. He also served on the Improving Quality Workgroup of Governor Kaine's Health Reform Commission. He has testified before state and federal hearings, including the U.S. Senate Judiciary Committee and U.S. Department of Labor. He serves on numerous advisory boards, including the board of commissioners of the Certification Commission for Health Information Technology (CCHIT).

Prior to joining the Center, Mr. Merritt was with America's Health Insurance Plans. He earned his master's degree in political science and government from Loyola University in Chicago, and he earned his bachelor's degree from Western Michigan University.